THE ECOLOGICAL CITIZEN

THE ECOLOGICAL CITIZEN

THE ECOLOGICAL CITIZEN:

*Good Earthkeeping
in America*

Dirck Van Sickle

PERENNIAL LIBRARY
Harper & Row, Publishers
New York, Evanston, San Francisco, London

First PERENNIAL LIBRARY edition published 1971.

STANDARD BOOK NUMBER: 06–080211–1

LIBRARY OF CONGRESS CATALOG CARD NUMBER: 74–159639

Poetry's the eagle
Flying from the forest,
Literature and lions
Run before the beaters;
Rhyming lines and leopards
Darting through the jungle,
Dropping like the buffalo,
Clubbed to death like seals:
Grass that won't be eaten
Feels the steel of science,
Psychology hunts tigers
With big-game degrees
    And gives the young
    Transistor tongues.

For Sylvia, with love and time

Contents

Foreword   xiii
Introduction: Who Ate Tomorrow?   xv

ONE: THE RUDE AWAKENING   1
   The Biotic Film: The Layer of Life   1
   U.S.S. *Earth*   5
   U.S.S. *Earth II*   11
   The Fusion Torch   15
   Mineral Bankruptcy   21
   Future Fossils   35
   Water Resources: the Planned Famine   39
   Timber Trends: Shaving the Planet   48
   The Continuing Energy Crisis   58
   Food: America's Anomaly   65
   Protein Piracy   78

TWO: MAKING ENDS MEET IN THE GROSS NATIONAL PRODUCT   83
   The Eternal Depression   83

De-advertising the Gross National Product   89
Reusable Rose   100
Discovering the Lost Trash Mine   103
Our Packaged Society   107
The Song of the Plastic Bottle   113
Newspaper—Save the Paper, Change the News   119
Trash Is Cash   125
On to the Recycled Society   130

THREE: MOVING SOCIETY AND TURNING THE FUTURE   139
Action and Reaction versus a Behavioral Laser   139
They're Doing It in Sweden   145
Start with a Stamp   149
Local Action Groups   158

FOUR: FEEDING THE FAMILY   167
Food Action No. 1: Clean It Up   167
Food Action No. 2: Buy Less of It   173
Food Action No. 3: Kitchen Conservation   177

FIVE: PREVENTING SOLID WASTE BY SAVING MONEY   183
Reusing Containers—Metal and Glass   183
The Plastic Paradox   186
Reusing Paper   189
Reusing Fabric   193
Around the House   197

SIX: BUILDING ECOLOGICAL SYSTEMS   203
Disposing of Sewage Disposal   203
Ecological Washday   212
Whiter-Than-White versus Greener-Than-Green   219
The Body Ecologic   222
In the Garden   228

SEVEN: DEFENDING ECOLOGICAL SYSTEMS   239
  Energy Ecotips and Kilowatt Capers   239
  Energy Ecotips and Infernal Combustion   246
  Protecting Ourselves from Urban Air   251
  Urban Defense Against Poisoned Ears   261
  Poisoning the Last Well   270
  Wildlife and the Smell of Smoke: A Final Chapter   278

Foreword

As the last decade matured, environmental awareness evolved from aesthetics (saving the last redwoods), to ecological stewardship (trying to save oil-soaked birds), until in late 1970 it became clear to everyone that our survival was itself at stake. America's rivers are septic, some carry nearly every water-borne germ known to man; our nation's air holds almost 1,000 pounds of poison for each of us. When we awakened from the long post-World War II American Dream, it was into a nightmare present of burning rivers, sterile species, and eternal trash.

This book is not about pollution per se, although we cannot ignore this dramatic signal of a greater evil. Fairfield Osborn wrote that waste is a resource out of place. Modern pollution breeds resources into each other—sulphur into air, phosphorus into water—at such a rate that the "average" American, who is twenty-six and could probably live fifty more years, will see the end of the resources we've always taken for granted. If we only "control" pollution at "tolerable" levels but don't stop the drain on resources, it will be a brief victory for this generation only.

The first third of this book describes resource consumption and how long certain resources will last. The rest is a program to answer the question "What can I do now?" on individual and group levels. Most of the suggestions describe altering individual lifestyle to lower our personal tax on the environment.

We finally saw the reality of the present during the 1960s. Now we must see the ecological *future* in time to prevent it, if there is to be a human future extending beyond this century.

Dirck Van Sickle
New York City

Introduction:

Who Ate Tomorrow?

"The end of the human race will be that it will eventually die of civilization." —Ralph Waldo Emerson

The quality of American life has grown abrasive at an increasing rate, especially in the cities, since the end of World War II and alarmingly so during the last decade. Daily existence is continually more costly, but less healthy, more stressful, insecure, uncohesive—a commercialized present with no united vision of tomorrow.

We spend extra for food and drink engineered to have minimal nutritional value because we're sold on being young and thin. But our government says that half of all Americans are poorly nourished and that malnutrition and, in some cases, starvation exist in the South and West and even the urban North. We can rarely read a food label without wondering what BHA is, or what diglyceride does. At least these mysteries are listed—we have no way of knowing if the food also contains pesticides, antibiotics, or other unintended adulterants. Our children have probably never known any other kind of food. Adulteration is somehow integral in our lifestyle, although we don't know why this need be so, or why a spectator culture "pleasantly plump" on animal protein is dying of heart disease.

America's number-one city has always been New York, where 200 cars were abandoned on the street every day during 1970 and a million extra wads of chewing gum and blobs of spittle flecked the sidewalks, already crowded by tons of garbage and litter, replacing the filth washed into the sewer by the previous day's 2,000 gallons of dog urine. The air tastes acid when it's misty, and it is clearly visible nearly every day, so thick it filters out up to 50 percent of the sunlight. Carbon monoxide displaces lighter oxygen in a thickening layer over the sidewalk. Blood seeps rather slowly through the brain and must enter with enough oxygen to nourish obscure cell communities at the ends of tiny blood vessels. Blood absorbs carbon monoxide more readily than oxygen to support all the brain's cells, and those that die are never replaced. Carbon monoxide poisoning loosens one's sense of time and causes perceptions to dysfunction; at high levels, you die, at lower New York City levels, you're short of breath, weak, irritable, plagued with headaches. Still, we spent nineteen times more on space travel than on mass transit and six times more on new highways than on air and water pollution during 1970.

Ninety-nine percent of America's electrified houses have TV, but there's no cultural unity because of this. More than ever, the young and their elders cannot communicate. While we spend over $2,300 a second on defense, school bond issues have failed in community after community in recent years, and some schools have closed for lack of funds. Education is no longer as conducive to social communication as it was; more and more, education is merely training for a salary. The ability to read is the essential requirement for learning anything. According to James E. Allen, Jr., U.S. Commissioner of Education, 75 percent of New York City's juvenile offenders are at least two years retarded in reading, and half the jobless under eighteen are "functionally illiterate." Allen also said that a quarter of the American student population has serious reading problems, while half the students in big-city schools read below grade level, and fully 68 percent of draftees read below seventh-grade level.[1] When all the students now in school have graduated, there will be 12 million more functionally illiterate Americans; there are 24 million now who are not in school.

Without communication, social cooperation for change seems almost impossible; without change, our ecological future is bleak indeed. George Wald, Nobel Prize biochemist, said that the end of civilization could come in fifteen to thirty years if we cannot come together to control population and pollution: "The problem is quality of life, and that quality has already deteriorated within this century."[2] Yet, what we are ravaging the environment to maintain is not a high standard of *living*, but rather a high standard of *consumption*, originally encouraged to maintain the high production levels achieved during World War II. The war was like economic amphetamine, and it ended the Great Depression, but when the end of war closed the Pacific and European dumping grounds to our economy, planned obsolescence

1. Reported in the New York *Post*, September 23, 1969.
2. Reported in the *New York Times*, November 19, 1970.

was introduced as a substitute. The high level of thrift encouraged during wartime was not only ended, but reversed, and the adult postwar generation went on a consumer binge unprecedented in history.

We are expected to maintain this binge not only today, but into the future, although it is frighteningly clear what the binge has produced. David Brower, who founded Friends of the Earth, calls it "cirrhosis of the environment."

Our economic system plans on having 50 percent more cars on the road in ten years, yet we know that even with the strictest controls, the total number of new vehicles will cause more automobile exhaust pollution than we have today. In ten years we also plan on paving 10 million more acres of land; in fact, our planning is so expansive that there will actually be, by the year 2000, a land deficit of 110 million acres,[3] an area greater than West Virginia and Montana combined. What this means is that while geography is limited, our plans are not. Traditionally, the economic planners have won; will *we* be able to eschew our economic plans when they conflict with conservation plans? What's posterity done for us? Conservation doesn't register in the Gross National Product.

Changing American lifestyle is a big job, yet unless we stop being GNP-minded and become planet-minded, there seems no way at all of surviving our planned future. GNP rises only from the ashes of earth's limited life support, including minerals as well as plants and animals, and the supply is much smaller than we think.

3. Hans H. Landsberg, Leonard L. Fishman, and Joseph L. Fisher, *Resources In America's Future* (Baltimore: Johns Hopkins, 1963), p. 24.

Furthermore, life support belongs not just to humans or Americans, although in that order we consume by far the greatest share, but to all life on Earth, of which we are only a troublesome part. As things are, Earth and Mother Nature can no longer afford to indulge the American Dream, just as they couldn't afford the grossness of dinosaurs. We'd better awaken from this dream, and we can best start by looking briefly into the sun.

THE ECOLOGICAL CITIZEN

One: The Rude Awakening

The Biotic Film: The Layer of Life

The mass of Earth's plant and animal life—biotic film—is roughly comparable to the film of an ant smeared over a basketball.

The thickness of the biotic film depends upon the nutrients available for its support. Unless another planet collides with ours, Earth will never have more life supplies than it does now. The total biotic film cannot increase, although components of the film may vary. Over the eons mammals have increased their ratio in the biotic film at the expense of plant life. During the past few million years, man has increased his proportion, at the expense of all other living things.

The mineral nutrients of Earth could not by themselves support life; there must be a constant supply of energy. Earth is supplied by a tremendous power plant, our sun, whose sustained hydrogen fusion generates 5.6 quintillion calories of heat every minute.[1] Mercury is too

1. Isaac Asimov, *The Neutrino* (New York: Dell, 1966), p. 213.

close to this furnace; Pluto is too far away; but Earth seems to be in just the right place. Naturally, not all the calorie output hits the Earth, and much of what does is fortunately reflected back into space by the oceans and icecaps. Of the calories which do remain within Earth's system, much energy is spent driving the currents in the ocean and atmosphere, but a tremendous amount fuels the biotic film. The eminent food scientist and author Georg Borgstrom assesses the energy involved in Earth's photosynthesis to be on the order of 250 quadrillion calories.[2] This total photosynthesis, the conversion of elements to organic matter, is the life support for the entire biotic film. Roughly twice as much of this conversion takes place in the ocean as on land. If we reduce the amount of green matter on earth, the total conversion of solar calories to food calories will drop: cut a forest and the sunlight fueling the formation and growth of trees will simply be heat reflected off bare ground. If we load the atmosphere with pollutants, such as smoke, which blocks incoming sunlight, there will also be a drop in photosynthesis. Mankind is actively involved in reducing photosynthesis through both methods—although the biotic film cannot be thickened very much, it can be thinned, and this is exactly the effect we are producing.

These numbers are only good for judging the mighty proportions of energy behind the biotic film; the ratio can be summarized by saying that for each 22.4 billion calories generated by the sun, only one becomes food within the biotic film. The most important proportion, in terms of mankind, is how much of the basic calorie

2. Georg Borgstrom, *The Hungry Planet* (New York: Macmillan, 1965), p. 60.

production of the biotic film is required for food by our species. If we each required only 2000 primary calories, there could in theory be over 12 trillion humans feeding directly from the primary photosynthesis of the planet.

But man cannot eat directly at the primary-calorie baseline; our food requires long chains of organisms to concentrate food energy for us. Most higher forms of life feed high on the food chain. The pelican, for example, eats fish which have eaten other fish which have eaten still smaller fish which ate one-celled animals which may have eaten one-celled plants, or plankton. Thus, from plankton to pelican, a great food chain exists which requires many primary calories for each "finished" calorie eaten by the pelican.

Professor Borgstrom calculates that mankind's finished calories require almost 20 percent of all land calorie production and nearly 14 percent of all the calories produced in the sea. The fine focusing from solar calories to man's food becomes shockingly sharp: our species requires for its feeding one out of every seven primary calories produced in the ocean and one calorie from every five produced on land. This doesn't include the plant calories man takes but doesn't eat, such as forest products and cotton fiber. If we double our numbers in thirty years mankind will then require, according to Dr. Borgstrom, "about 40 percent of the earth's total plant production for its immediate dietary needs. As already hinted, man would in reality need more than this." [3] By the year 2000, we will have to usurp close to half the total life support for Earth's entire biotic film.

Higher forms of life can exist only because of the

3. Borgstrom, *The Hungry Planet*, p. 60.

tremendous complexity of lifeforms within the biotic film; the diversity of lifeforms provides a failsafe, a cushion, that until modern times has been able to absorb the excesses of any single species. Simply, within a rich, broad spectrum of lifeforms, the total biota can adjust and readjust its mix of species and in this way remain balanced and stable. When the complexity of lifeforms is reduced, the total system is simplified and becomes much more vulnerable to complete collapse. A small example is the simplification, through agriculture, of a complex plant and animal community into a large mono-crop—say, 300 acres of corn. With the biotic community thus simplified to one plant species, animals and other plants which maintained a balanced population of pest insects are gone, and one pest insect grows in number with nothing to stop it as it consumes its specific food, the corn. To stop the pest, we amplify and simplify pest control with chemical pesticides. DDT used to control pests has leaked through the biotic film and produced disasters such as the reproduction failure among California and Gulf Coast pelicans. This is alarming to us because we eat from the same links of the food chain as does the pelican. Often, the entire single crop species is suddenly blighted by a single virus; the Irish potato famine and the 1970 Midwest corn crop are examples.

It has been said that for a new pound of human flesh to appear, a pound of some other form of life must disappear. As our human mass doubles to 400 million tons, 200 million more tons of other life will have to go. An example is the destruction of the buffalo, done not only to destroy the Plains Indian but also to free the prairies for crops and grazing. We have worn the biotic film dangerously thin by simplifying it for our benefit. In loose terms, we will have to eliminate as much other life by 2000 as the human race weighs today if our population is to double. In reality, because we eat so high on the food chains, we will have to get rid of a lot more than merely the equivalent weight of our species. As noted, the simplification will have to be so thorough by 2000 as to "free up" more than 40 percent of Earth's total calorie production for our own feeding.

We mine the biotic film at our great peril, no less so because of the careless way we simplify membership within the biotic community. Think how long it's taken Earth to develop a biotic film rich enough to permit our late development, yet look at the brief geologic instant between now and A.D. 2000 in which we, in order to continue our present path of development, will have to simplify this complexity almost twice as much as we already have. Earth's organic resources cannot provide an American standard of consumption for many more people than already enjoy it; ecologists doubt that our country will be able to maintain its biotic demand, or the rest of humanity its miserable status quo, for very much longer. Mankind is demanding far too great a share of common life support, an inordinate share for one species to consume. Because of the amount we require, and the thoughtless way we take it, the entire biotic film has already lost its balance and is showing signs of coming apart.

U.S.S. *Earth*

If Adlai Stevenson is indeed responsible for coining the concept "Spaceship Earth," I doubt he intended his gentle statement about our survival depending on caring for and loving our planetary home to come to mean it should be thought of as an organic "machine" whose functioning can be manipulated for our sole benefit. Nonetheless, we seem to consider our planet as U.S.S. *Earth*, United States registration; a biotic spacecraft whose stores are not only our own, but virtually unlimited.

Americans consume more global resources than the rest of the human race together—more minerals, energy, and food. In terms of food, about 500 million people on the spaceship travel first class—most of North America and Europe, primarily. Several hundred million more travel in a dwindling coach section. Most people travel steerage—two billion who together do not consume as much as the elite in first class. Steerage is swelling as more travelers from coach are impoverished; approximately 60 percent of humanity is slowly starving to death while first-class passengers debate whether or not there will be a famine and, if so, how soon. The death-by-starvation rate is between 10 and 20 million a year now; Paul Ehrlich, Stanford University population biologist, suggests the death rate will be between 100 and 200 million by 1980,[4] others have predicted global famine as early as 1975;[5] the consensus seems to indicate the 1980s. Certainly before 2000—in fact, a second and more severe global famine is predicted for the end of the century if the earlier one does not produce what biologists call a large enough dieback.

The chilly word "dieback" describes the ultimate in nature's control over an out-of-control species and means

4. Paul Ehrlich, *Mademoiselle*, April, 1970, p. 293.
5. William and Paul Paddock, *Famine, 1975!* (Boston: Little Brown, 1967).

the sudden death of a major portion of an exploding animal population. The causes are many and bewildering. Almost entire herds of deer on an island with sufficient food to sustain them have been observed to rapidly die back to a smaller number, more in tune with the ecology of their island. The deer didn't starve and there was no indication of epidemic. In lab experiments, trapped populations of mice—which explode in number very quickly—always end in dieback: their behavior degenerates or "sinks" rapidly to the abandonment and eating of young, homosexuality, lethargy or aggression, increased susceptibility to disease, stress-induced neurosis and psychosis, and other remarkable urban maladies before the dieback begins. After dying back to a reasonable number, the mice begin exploding all over again. If man is like mouse and if the first dieback of the 1980s doesn't catastrophically reduce our numbers, we could have a worse dieback around 2000.

As far as we know, we have never suffered global dieback, though it might be argued that the plagues of the Middle Ages were a kind of dieback—the cities grew too populous for their sanitation systems. Both of Dr. Borgstrom's books, as well as Paul Ehrlich's *The Population Bomb,* are among several which make clear that man is fast reaching the dieback point in terms of food supplies for major regions on Earth. Famine and plague work synergistically; the combination is inevitable and produces a much more severe effect than one would expect by assessing each factor separate from the other. Thus, a famine in Pakistan and India (or South America) would not, in this age of jet travel, be a contained disaster; its accompanying plague could easily be spread in a matter of days to the Northern Hemisphere.

These dark projections are the other side of the graph

that projects a 3- or 4-trillion-dollar American GNP for 2000. In trying to consume enough to fulfill this bright projection, we are speeding the inevitability of the dark one. In an article in the *New York Times*[6] Professor Ehrlich writes: "Ecological considerations indicate that only fifty million Americans, living as they do today, could eventually destroy the planet. And it is difficult to imagine any American lifestyle which would prevent three hundred million of us from accomplishing the same end in the long run."

We Americans create more global air and water pollution than do all the other people on the planet—about 210 million of us foul the planet more than do 3.3 billion others. Dr. Ehrlich, in the article mentioned above, estimates that if America increases by only 75 million during the next thirty years, this moderate increase will destroy more of the ecosystem than would 3.7 billion Indians born between now and 2000. Each American demands 50 times more than an Indonesian does, and, according to British naturalist, Peter Scott, we will each create 1,000 times more pollution than the average Asian.[7]

Because starving populations don't want to starve, we're faced with what has been called the revolution of rising expectations. For years we have tried to feed the rising expectations of India with technology and new agricultural practices as well as millions of tons of food. Yet even the richest nation cannot pacify the entire Third World, and the revolution is being courted by new powers, notably China with politics and Japan with business deals.

In America, the average age is twenty-six; but in

6. November 4, 1970.
7. Reported in the *New York Times*, November 18, 1970.

Brazil it is seventeen, and in most of the hungry nations half the population is under fifteen years of age—this is particularly true in Latin America, where up to 70 percent of the children in some countries are chronically malnourished. Protein starvation is the problem, and it is widespread in Africa as well as in Asia. Inadequate protein during fetal development and through the first six months of an infant's life can result in up to 60 percent fewer brain cells than normal. The brain grows very rapidly just after birth, and if the protein isn't there to supply cell formation, it will never take place, even if protein is available later. Because of protein starvation during infancy, the children in many South American, Asian, and African nations are called the "twilight generation."

Twilight generations exist in nearly every country projected to double its population before 2000. Brazil will double in twenty-two years, Peru in twenty-three, Costa Rica in twenty, El Salvador in nineteen. Kenya will double in twenty-four years, Nigeria in twenty-eight, Indonesia in thirty-one years—the malnourished under age fifteen is the area of greatest growth throughout the hungry Third World.[8] How will these nations fill a doubled demand for teachers, doctors, engineers—not to mention twice as much food and other resources—when the work force will be today's twilight generation grown up?

In 1968, the president of Pakistan, Mohammed Ayub Kahn, shocked the world by predicting humans would be eating humans in his country within 10 years. It is now a few years and a major disaster closer to that time

8. Paul R. Ehrlich, *The Population Bomb* (New York: Ballantine Books, 1968).

—will his prediction come true? Far from moving to answer that question in a negative way, Americans and other rich citizens of the world tend to shut it out, put their faith in the Rockefeller Foundation and the Green Revolution, and simply continue as ever before, aggravating the desperate nature of the situation by taking vital resources, including animal protein, from the hungry nations. Peru, like Pakistan, has a large twilight generation, yet takes the greatest tonnage of fish from the sea; it need sail forth only into the Humboldt Current to haul in more fish than any other nation. This incredibly rich current flows along the South American West Coast, which explains Peru's militant stance on her 200-mile territorial limit, but not why Peruvians are among the world's most protein-starved people.

The huge annual catch is almost all one species—anchoveta—and is reduced to fish-meal concentrate, a high-protein food. While taxing a single species so heavily will soon diminish it (the results of overfishing are already indicated by smaller catches), the overfishing might be justified if the fish actually did feed hungry Peruvians. Almost the entire output of fish meal is exported, however, primarily to Western Europe and America (we buy more than 25 percent) for use as pet and livestock food. It is used in "factory farming" to produce rapid animal growth, assisted with drugs. This is why the price of chicken is so low—the true price for our chicken dinner is paid by damaged Peruvian children.

In spite of domestic hunger and poor eating habits, which leave over half of even the more affluent undernourished, we are proud of our dietary standard—only the white populations of New Zealand, Australia, and Argentina consume more red meat per capita than Americans. Nonetheless we still consume more total animal protein than any other people on Earth. Before quotas stabilized beef prices, we imported 10 percent of our red meat from Mexico—a nation with a twilight generation. We import ocean animal protein, shrimp, for example, from hungry nations such as Ecuador, Taiwan, India, and Mexico. We *lead the world* in the importation of animal protein.

We have not been self-sufficient in food for quite some time; our only agricultural surpluses are cotton and tobacco. When we donate milk abroad, we must also buy it abroad. It is because of our role as number-one animal-protein consumer *and* importer that the revolution of rising expectations has made our future uneasy.

As we learned during the last decade, we cannot afford, in terms of social cohesion or money, to keep the steerage below decks by military might.

U.S.S. *Earth II*

As we sit in first class worrying about the rumbling below, another ship has been sighted on the horizon. It's about thirty years off and too far to tell for sure, but many believe it to be the U.S.S. *Earth II*, the new population created between now and 2000, which some believe will be a luxury ship and others believe will be riddled with plague.

It will be alongside in less than three decades, its grappling hooks clutching our vessel to it as it unloads the last of what we fear will be 4 billion new passengers. What will we do if 500 million of the newcomers expect to join us in first class? Will we provide them each with a lifetime supply of 10,000 pounds of meat and 28,000 pounds of milk? Will we be able to spare each new arrival his rightful 56 million gallons of water; will we allow the crowd free access to whatever shreds of forest may remain? [9] Even if we somehow can double the manifest for first class, there will still be twice as much steerage to worry about, and we'll still have only one planet's worth of life support to go around. How can we stretch one Earth's worth of an already short food supply to feed two Earth's worth of people?

Mankind and his livestock have already put a burden on the biotic film equivalent to that of 15 million people eating primary calorie production. If we try to maintain food standards while the population doubles, this will mean a doubled tax on food resources that are not sufficient to prevent more than 60 percent of humanity from living in constant hunger. Obviously, the human race as a whole will have to move closer to primary production to find its food. We can't expect Asiatics, Indians, Africans, South Americans, and others in the Third World to absorb population growth by eating lower on the food chain—most of them have been eating primary plant production for generations and simply cannot eat any closer to the baseline than they do now. Rice, a primary plant, is the main food for most of humanity; it is only first class that can afford to cut corners. No more fish meal for poultry feed, for example, and a greater proportion of vegetables, fruits, grains, and cereals in our diet. This shift to a lower link is already indicated

9. Robert Rienow and Leona Train Rienow, *Moment in the Sun* (New York: Ballantine Books, 1967), p. 3.

by the skyrocketing price of most animal protein and the recent diet changes urged to reduce the epidemic of heart attacks.

In order for mankind to lose enough environmental weight to survive the threatened dieback, first class will have to embark upon a strict primary, environmental diet. If the 1980s dieback occurs, it will largely be the fault of Americans and Europeans for having continued to consume the major portion of available food and other resources, energy included. It is our expensive lifestyle, not our numbers, which lie beneath the present problem. Global pollution is a negative factor in food production, and we create over half of this pollution, much of it through energy consumption.

America consumes 80 percent of the energy produced by all mankind. As it is the ocean cannot feed the world, and our energy consumption may cripple its future output. We have substantially raised the levels of lead, radiation, and carbon monoxide in the upper layer of the ocean, its most biologically active area. Even if we were not debilitating marine ecology, the number of people will outstrip per capita food production from the sea so that it is doubtful the ocean will provide proportionally as much food in 1980 as it did in 1970. The real menace is not so much the sulphur dioxide in our lungs as the gradual attrition of food resources, contaminated or eliminated by poison.

Much of our energy consumption is concentrated in the Eastern megalopolis, the urban strip from Boston to Washington to Atlanta, where supplying the energy demand has created a smog belt which has already begun to destroy great tracts of vegetation, including forest and crops. High energy consumption has produced the same effect on the West Coast. Yet indications are that energy demand will be 8 times as great by 2021.[10] We're already experiencing chronic "brownouts" in large urban areas because the power demand doubled during the 1960s, but the power supply did not. We are planning on increased power demand, but have no source of supply.

Hydropower is nearly at maximal use; supplies of gas and oil are too limited to provide even half the power produced today by coal. Today, coal supplies more electrical power than all other fuels combined and is expected to supply twice as much in 1985 as today and 4 times as much before 2021. When this happens, air pollution will blot out entire vast regions of the nation. Electric utilities have so far spent a total of $1 billion on air pollution, but by 2000 will have to spend between $450 million and $1.4 billion *every year* to control sulphur dioxide alone—the actual price will depend on how well we want to control it. All of this assumes nuclear energy to surpass coal by 1995, and that breeder reactors will be in use.[11] These super-fission reactors are very dangerous and highly experimental—as is regular fission reaction. Yet we plan our course to include nuclear-fired generating plants to supply over half our power by 2000.

The problem with energy is much the same as with food. In terms of energy, we are risking a great deal on the gamble that the U.S.S. *Earth II* will arrive not only with prodigious supplies of food magically obtained

10. Editors of *Fortune, The Environment* (New York: Harper & Row, 1970), p. 117.
11. *Ibid.*

from the ocean, but also with unlimited power from a hoped-for fusion reaction to bail us out of our projections.

The Fusion Torch

Perhaps the most pernicious pollution of the 1960s was the spate of technological projections, usually aimed at the year 2000 when the pie will come down from the sky because of scientific achievement.

As long as we believe the future to be the creation of technology rather than biology, there's no reason to reduce our ecological impact except insofar as we are discomforted by dirty air and water. We are promised that technology will even take care of this if only we will spend the money. Thus, our increasing consumption is "justified" and encouraged by the irresponsible promotion of a future rich in consumer goods.

Possibly the most incredible "future" is that of Colin Clark, Director of the Agricultural Economics Research Institute, Oxford, who believes current unease over the population explosion to be nonsense. He sees a world ahead which can provide "a diet containing meat and dairy products on a North American scale to 45,000 million [45 billion] people." [12] Energy supplies in this well-fed future are, of course, limitless, what with nu-

12. Colin Clark, *Man and his Future*, Gordon Wolstenholme, ed. (Boston: Little, Brown, 1963), p. 35.

clear power, solar batteries, and even hydrogen-driven cars. Not only could there be all the food and energy anyone can conceive of, but the 45 billion could, by merely mining the earth's crust to a depth of 1500 meters [a bit short of a mile], consume minerals at the present North American rate for "some multiple of 10^5 [hundreds of thousands of] years." [13]

It is never made clear where we'd put the biotic film as we peeled back the earth's crust, or how we would make traditionally poor soil outproduce Iowa—or, for that matter, why it is that most of humanity cannot even subsist as things are now.

Drs. Harrison Brown, Michael E. DeBakey, and Alvin M. Weinberg described the future to a convention of the American Society of Newspaper Editors recently.[14] Professor Brown of the California Institute of Technology predicted a possible 15 billion world population around the end of the century—but not a happy population. Pointing out that there are already 500 million more "hungry, combustible human beings" now than ten years ago, he projected that this "will increase by at least another 600 million" before 1980 as the gap between the fed and the starving continues to widen. If 15 billion seems unbelievable for just a few years after 2000, consider that in the late 1950s the century was projected to end with 5 billion people; in the mid-1960s, the United Nations estimates slowly rose from 6 billion to 6.5 billion. Now the UN says 7.5 billion. Population projections have consistently been proved low; if there is no early dieback, perhaps we will be estimating 8 billion in a few years, or even 8.5 billion. If there is no

13. *Ibid.*
14. Reported in the *New York Times*, April 23, 1967.

dieback, projections put world population over 15 billion by about 2025.

Dr. DeBakey, the famous heart surgeon, predicted that when heart disease and cancer are dealt with, "there is no reason why a person can't live to be 100 to 150 years old." Death control without birth control has brought us the population problems we face today; imagine what *real* death control could mean! Even if we press birth control as vigorously as possible, world population is not expected to stabilize until around 2045. It will not be the hungry of the earth living to a ripe old 150, it will be the first-class high consumers—each of whom will have an additional eighty years, a second lifetime, in which to consume and pollute.

Dr. Weinberg, Atomic Energy Commission's Oak Ridge Laboratory director, in typical AEC style, destroyed any sober thoughts the previous scientists might have inspired regarding the relationship of thrift to survival. Breeder reactors, Dr. Weinberg predicted, will save the race by burning "the rocks and the dirt" and thereby keep all mankind going with 50 times today's energy "not for 100 or 1,000 years, but essentially forever, literally millions and millions of years." Naturally, the magic atom will also desalt the ocean to provide water and hydrogen to fertilize giant desert agrocomplexes to feed, as well as electrify, the world of 2000.

Breeder reactors are fission types, that is, they create energy by splitting heavy-element uranium into plutonium (the "bred" fuel) as well as a long list of highly poisonous radioactive elements. The difference between today's fission reactors and the breeder is chiefly the creation of a far greater proportion of plutonium in the broken-down uranium by speeding the atomic reaction at much higher temperatures. This is much faster than normal fission and far, far more dangerous. There are at present no breeder reactors operating in the United States; the experimental fast-breeders have had to be closed down because of near-disastrous accidents. Critics say that if regular fission is untested and hazardous, breeder reactors pose far greater odds for catastrophe— yet our official planning seems to take breeders for granted when projecting our energy demand. During the 1930s it was similarly taken for granted that everyone would be flying "autogyros" instead of driving automobiles by the middle 1940s.

The fusion reaction is what is called the fusion torch; the final and most eternal power source. Fusion is the power of the stars. Fission splits heavy uranium atoms; fusion combines light atoms of hydrogen into heavier atoms and releases untold amounts of energy as well as pollution in the process. The fuel for fusion is deuterium, which exists as one-thousandth of all the earth's water. Fuel would be incredibly cheap, if only the 50-million-degree operating temperatures can be sustained. Because sustained fusion is still only theoretical, we have even less information on the possibilities of its pollution than we have for fission, but one possibly is that all the earth's water could become modified by tritium, a fusion waste which would not merely contaminate water, but would become an integral part of it. The development of fusion technology is one of the most exciting of science's leading edges, but if it is premature to rely on nuclear fission, it would be sheer lunacy to count on fusion to bail us out of our consumption pattern.

Understand that all this is not intended to be anti-scientific; like most critics of the premature spread of nuclear technology, I hope some form of atomic energy will be clean and certain enough for public use within our lifetime. The problem is that we do not have such atomic energy now and should not take its appearance in the near future for granted.

Perhaps the most comprehensive study of energy and resource demands and supplies until 2000 is *Resources in America's Future*, by Hans H. Landsberg, Leonard L. Fishman, and Joseph L. Fisher, of Resources for the Future, Inc., a nonprofit corporation funded by the Ford Foundation to constantly assess America's on-going resource patterns.[15] The authors show the following pattern in fuel sources from the recent past to the century's end:

Percentage of fuel used in	1960	1980	2000
coal	53.7	47.1	29.6
gas and oil	28.7	22.3	11.7
nuclear	0.0	17.9	51.1

Although the amount of coal burned will have fallen to not quite half today's percentage, the actual tonnage will be about three times more than is burned now because of greatly increased total fuel consumption. The percentage of nuclear fuel will be more than half the total by 2000, or about the same percentage as coal holds in today's consumption. Yet, in 1960, nuclear energy provided no fuel at all, and in 1970 it provided less than one percent. Gas and oil are not being phased out in favor of nuclear energy because of nuclear energy's "air pollution advantage"—if this were so, we should drop coal most rapidly; the real reason is that there won't be enough oil and gas to play even one-half the

15. Hans H. Landsberg, Leonard L. Fishman, Joseph L. Fisher, *Resources in America's Future* (Baltimore: Johns Hopkins, 1963).

role they do today. Thus, we seem committed to the phenomenal rise of nuclear energy from one percent of x to 51 percent of 8x in thirty years.

Even though nuclear energy poses a hazard no one—not even the AEC—denies, we must develop it because our consumption patterns show us exhausting current petroleum reserves by 2000.

Comparing our fuel consumption to India's is always unconvincing because no one, especially the Indians, wants to live at such low levels; nonetheless, the 6 percent of men who are Americans consume over 50 percent of man's fuel, while 15 percent who are Indians consume only 1.5 percent. If fission's radioactive zoo is loosed into the common environment, it will not be because of the needs of the many, but because of the extravagant lifestyle of the few.

It's been said that we develop resources the way a small boy "develops" his mother's supply of jam. In this case, the jam belongs to mankind and the future; because no more can be gotten from the supermarket, our supply must last. Yet, America has burned half the oil ever consumed and 90 percent of the natural gas. To find more, we must rip into the ocean and tundra. Because we haven't had to reach so far to "develop" supplies until now, no one can predict the global damage of oil pollution in two such important environments.

Still, the fossil fuels will be exhausted before our demand will, and we are urged to nuclear power by government policy and by industry. General Electric, which makes reactors, recently headlined an ad: "Light a match. And you put more smoke in the air than a nuclear power plant." Two AEC brochures—"Genetic Effects of Radiation" and "Fallout from Nuclear Tests"—indicate that present standards for atomic plants can ultimately increase birth defects and cancer by 10 percent, meaning 8,000 more birth defects and 32,000 more cases of cancer every year. The government recently stopped construction of two nuclear plants on Biscayne Bay because they would have drawn all the water in the bay through their systems every month to provide cooling, in the process cooking microscopic lifeforms and dumping them back into the heated bay as dead organic refuse.

A match may put more smoke in the air than a nuclear plant, but it's not the smoke hazard we must consider as we accept, to satisfy our inordinate lifestyle, the tremendous gamble whose debt our children will have to pay if we lose.

Mineral Bankruptcy

"Americans are faced with a new and strange emergency. Certain of the richest mineral resources of the nation are in alarming danger of exhaustion. Conservationists have from time to time urged care in using this or that raw material lest present-day extravagance impoverish future generations. Yet the enormous rate of depletion of natural deposits of economic minerals . . . brings impoverishment of some of them so close that the present generation must do something about it for its own protection."

—D. H. Killeffer, Chemical Engineer and Contributing Editor, *Scientific American*, January, 1944

D. H. Killeffer's twenty-five-year-old warning has long ago come true; his "present generation" did little for its own, or our, protection. The high wartime production was what Killeffer called "present-day extravagance," but that production didn't stop with the war—it was just diverted to the consumer front. Domestic mineral resources to support our peacetime war economy were officially pronounced dead by the Paley Commission, charged by President Truman to assess our domestic resource reserves. The commission termed us a "have-not nation" twenty years ago.

Our trillion-dollar GNP, almost equal to the rest of the world combined, is produced in large part from imported resources. Not that we have no important ores remaining, but we have exhausted our rich deposits and have only second-grade and low-grade deposits which make it cheaper to import prime ores primarily from the hungry nations. If we could not "develop" the mineral resources of poorer nations, it is doubtful we could sustain our standard of living for as long as five years. With the possible exception of the vast Soviet Union, all other industrialized nations are in a similar position. As our consumption continues to increase, our dependence on the underdeveloped grows. Much of the world's manganese, platinum, chromium, and nickel are in Communist, or at least politically unstable, areas; and because wars are not really fought over ideology, but for resources, our hopes for world peace seem unsoundly based.

Tin comes from Southeast Asia and Bolivia, lead from Peru, aluminum ore and copper from South America and Africa. Our government often feels it necessary to intervene in the politics of our supplier nations, sometimes to the extent of supporting military dictatorships. We must keep our supply lines open, and often this means putting down the revolution of rising expectations. If it weren't for Chilean copper, perhaps we wouldn't be so concerned about their recent election of a Marxist president.

All industrialized nations depend on suppliers, and Japan, perhaps the most intensely industrialized country on earth, even includes the United States among her resource colonies to an extent which goes far beyond the recycling of our scrap iron. U.S. Plywood–Champion holds a fifty-year contract with the Forest Service to log Alaska's Tongass National Forest for 8.75 billion board feet. In spite of cries from the timber industry that shortages demand immediate increased logging of national forests, the wood from Tongass is slated for export to Japan. Imagine a single plank a foot wide and an inch thick which circles the earth 66 times and you get an idea of the size of this resource sale. It takes a forest that far north about a century to regrow; this can hardly be called the sale of a "renewable" resource.

Japan has also signed numerous long-term contracts for American coal, one of which demands 1.5 million tons of high-grade low-sulphur "smokeless" coal each year. In this case, the mineral rights to the coal, which lies under a national forest in West Virginia, are directly controlled by the Japanese. Japan exploits even the exploiters; she has no commercial forest and, being the world's most polluted country, sorely needs low-pollution coal for her steel mills (Nippon Steel is now bigger than U.S. Steel). If Japan can get what she needs from us, it's only in the best American tradition.

Charles F. Parks, Jr., professor of geology and mineral engineering at Stanford University, feels today's world population may already be well past the number our planet can support. Should Asia, Africa, and South America become industrialized even to a fraction of our degree, the sudden surge in resource demand would create an immediate global shortage. Should a doubled population in 2000 demand minerals at the levels we did in 1967, Dr. Parks estimates annual iron ore demand to be 12 times today's level. Copper demand, which Dr. Parks decribes as already staggering, would be 12 times greater; lead, already in shortage, would be 16 times more in demand. Supplying these minerals at such levels would be, according to Dr. Parks, "a difficult and probably an impossible task." [16] His calculations assume that metal consumption in industrialized nations would not rise above 1967 levels. The assumption is, of course, rhetorical—we're consuming the lion's share of minerals today, and our projected consumption requires that we continue to do so.

It is difficult to conceive of future metal demand unless put into historical perspective. Consider all the metal mined and used from the beginning of history to 1900: projections indicate that between now and 2000 we will consume about 8 times as much metal as the entire amount produced prior to 1900. This colossal increase will be boosted even further if undeveloped nations attempt to industrialize. Should this happen, we would probably find much of our supply drying up as mineral resources are diverted for domestic consumption in our supplier nations.

Although our own population is expected to grow by no more than 1.5 percent a year, our metal consumption is expected to increase by 3.1 percent annually. At present, American per capita metal consumption is about 7 tons; if we meet projected demands, by 2000 we will

16. Reported in the *New York Times*, June 22, 1969.

each be consuming 15 tons. Per capita metal consumption is expected to continue growing after that, eventually reaching 100 tons. Meeting this increased personal demand will require depleting almost all the known commercial ore deposits, certainly all high-grade deposits, in the world.

Industrialization will be impossible for underdeveloped nations, even if they overcome food and population problems, without metal. If not for the rich mineral deposits in the Western states, the United States couldn't have industrialized as rapidly as it did. As we have seen, we did so at the expense of our own commerical grades of ore and must now import much of what we consume. Because minerals are not renewable resources, it is criminal to continue lifestyles and consumption patterns which will not only leave future generations destitute but will create emergencies before the century ends.

The story of minerals is the same as with food and energy; it is not the collective demand of the many which is depleting supplies; it is the inordinate demand of the few. Because Americans make up nearly half the total of this few, we more than any other people should effect a change in consumption to make possible continuing metal supplies at least throughout our own age and hopefully well into the next generation.

To focus more closely on this urgent need for thrift, let's briefly survey the present and expected supply and demand of our nine most important metals.

The figures below are adapted from *Resources in America's Future;* all figures have been standardized to short tons (2,000 pounds each).[17] Although the figures

17. Landsberg, et al., *Resources,* pp. 293–316, 427–471.

themselves are important, this magnitude staggers comprehension; the most important thing to look for is the proportion of growth indicated—the figures have been set up to facilitate quick scanning for this purpose.

In some cases the terms "Communist" and "non-Communist" world are used. The authors of *Resources* use these terms, although I would rather the only distinctions made were between America and the rest of the world. The ideological distinctions can be misleading; we trade with some Communist nations: does this make them part of the non-Communist supply? Political sides often change; Chile "went Communist" since the estimates were made for the non-Communist world's copper supply (Chile is the world's largest copper exporter). In any event, the distinction has been maintained because in some cases a non-Communist figure is given in *Resources* without the supplemental Communist world figure.

The calculations are based on consumption during the 1960s, which means that we are already well into the *cumulative demand*, the total amount of metal that will have been used between 1960 and 2000. *Resources* gives both a "medium" and a "high" projection; high projections are indicated by (H); all other figures are the medium projection.

Important terms relating to supply are *reserves* and *potential*. "Reserves" indicates the amount of ore now available which is of sufficiently high metal content to be commercially exploited. Potential ore, like the fusion torch, is a big "maybe." Potential ore includes the proven reserves, plus ore whose metal content is too low to be profitably exploited or which will require a technological breakthrough before it can produce any metal, plus unproven estimated reserves.

Iron and Steel

We import a third of our iron ore, mostly from Venezuela and Canada; Brazil, with 60 percent of the world's high-grade iron ore, is hoped to be our chief future supply. Because iron and steel make up 90 percent of our metal use, we are most interested in Brazil's internal politics and future alignments.

U.S. Iron Consumption:		*million tons*
	1960—	72
	1980—	121
	2000—	194
		378 (H)

U.S. Cumulative Demand:	*billion tons*
	4.7
	7.2 (H)
U.S. Iron Reserves:	3.4
U.S. Iron Potential:	26.0

As we can see, we do not have enough reserves to supply our medium cumulative demand, which is no problem as long as foreign supplies remain available. If these are cut off, we could survive by cutting consumption (drastically), increasing recycling, and, certainly, by raising steel prices. Of all metals, the future supplies of iron and steel are the brightest, even though we must look beyond our borders to realize them.

Aluminum

Although aluminum comprises about 7 percent of the earth's crust, only bauxite ore is high enough in metal content to make aluminum packaging possible. Working different potential ores would mean high-cost aluminum. Ten years ago we were consuming 40 percent of the planet's bauxite production; we had to import 98.2 percent of this. We have only about five years' worth of bauxite in America, the rest seems to be in Africa and South America. Italians use 5 pounds of aluminum per capita each year; we use 22 pounds. Aluminum is 6 percent of our total metal consumption, but by 2000 its importance will have tripled, and it will constitute about 18 percent.

		million tons
U.S. Aluminum Consumption:	1960—	1.6
	1980—	5.7
	2000—	14.7
		31.1 (H)
U.S. Cumulative Demand:		255
		480 (H)
U.S. Aluminum Reserves:		13
U.S. Aluminum Potential:		98

We'd better not count on meeting the projection that we each use 4.1 pounds of aluminum for foils and tubes in 2000 unless we intend to buy up several supplier nations. Very few other things are slated to grow between 1,400 and 3,100 percent during the next thirty years.

Obviously, we will have to look elsewhere for our aluminum ore; not even our potential comes close to meeting cumulative demand. Total cumulative demand for the non-Communist world is put at 900 million tons by 2000, but total non-Communist world reserves are only 800 million tons. Communist reserves are only about 100 million tons, so even total world conquest would not assure a supply which would satisfy demand for this vital metal. Obviously, consumption will have to be reduced as well as vast new bauxite deposits found.

Copper

Commerical copper ore contained 3 percent metal in the 1880s; by the 1930s metal content had fallen to 1.6 percent; during the 1950s it was a measly 0.8 percent and is no doubt lower now. Needless to say, we import a great deal of what we consume.

		million tons
U.S. Copper Consumption:	1960—	1.8
	1980—	3.6
	2000—	5.8
		14.0 (H)
U.S. Cumulative Demand:		112
		181 (H)
U.S. Copper Reserves:		50
U.S. Copper Potential:		100

Chile is the world's leading copper supplier, and foreign copper consumption exceeds our own, so the competition for available ore will grow. Total world reserves are about 270 million tons, of which the non-Communist world holds 250 million tons. Total non-Communist world cumulative demand will be 560 million tons by 2000; 50 percent difference between supply and the demand is the motive behind much of our current world politics.

Lead and Zinc

Because these minerals are usually found together, consumption figures for them have been combined. Unlike the previous mentioned ores, lead and zinc must be mined underground like gold, so not enough is known of potential supplies to provide even an estimate. We have been importing 60 percent of our zinc and 40 percent of our lead, and we are now critically short of lead.

		million tons
U.S. Lead and Zinc Consumption:	1960—	1.9
	1980—	3.3
	2000—	5.7
		12.1 (H)
U.S. Cumulative Demand:		105
		194 (H)
U.S. Lead and Zinc Reserves:		29.5

World lead reserves of 80 million tons aren't enough to cover even non-Communist demand; our own medium cumulative lead demand by 2000 will consume half the total world supply. Presumably, the rest of the non-Communist world will want as much as we do, but it won't be there. And if the Communists want some, too. . . . World zinc reserves mainly in South America are 140 million tons; non-Communist cumulative demand by 2000 will require 170 million tons. A negative supply, not even counting Communist zinc demands.

Manganese

A perfect example of a no-substitute, short-supply metal is manganese, a hardening alloy essential in all steel making. Even if the North American Continent were 100 percent iron ore, we could have no steel without manganese, about 35 pounds of which are required for each ton of steel. U.S. *potential* looks good, but again, it is only potential, requiring proof, technological breakthrough, and/or raised steel prices.

		million tons
U.S. *Manganese Consumption*:	1960—	1.1
	1980—	2.0
	2000—	3.2
		5.8 (H)
U.S. *Cumulative Demand*:		82.0
		120.0 (H)
U.S. *Manganese Reserves*:		1.0
U.S. *Manganese Potential*:		88.0

Even if we could develop our potential, it would barely cover our own needs. Our reserves are hopelessly inadequate. Non-Communist world demand for 300 million tons by 2000 will not be met with the non-Communist world supply of only 200 million tons. The Communist world has about 250 million tons, most of it in Russia, more than they'll need. We may have to look to the Soviets for future supplies.

Nickel

Nickel is a vital alloy with over 3,000 applications and use is rapidly growing. Some alloys are 99 percent nickel. Use of nickel in stainless steel is slated to go from 25 pounds per ton at present to 35 pounds by 2000. A steady, and vastly increasing supply will be required.

		million tons
U.S. *Nickel Consumption*:	1960—	0.1
	1980—	4.1
	2000—	11.8
U.S. *Cumulative Demand*:		11.8
		19.5 (H)
U.S. *Nickel Reserves*:		0.5

American supplies of nickel are dismally shorter than any other important mineral. Note that the medium cumulative demand figure is the same as the 2000 consumption figure (also medium projection). This indicates that the higher figure for cumulative demand may be the more realistic.

By the year 2000, nickel demand by the non-Communist world will require a supply of 37 million tons. The non-Communist world supply is, however, only 11.3 million tons. Cuba has a tremendous amount of nickel, but since that supply closed to us, we have had to depend on Canadian reserves. How the non-Communist world will get by on a third of what it needs is not clear.

Tungsten

Because tungsten has the highest melting point of any metal, it is vital to technological society. Without it, there'd be no light bulbs, jet engines, high-grade machine tools, space shots, or even nuclear reactors. But look at these figures:

		thousand tons
U.S. Tungsten Consumption:	1960—	4.5
	1980—	10.0
	2000—	23.0
		38.0 (H)
U.S. Cumulative Demand:		460.0
		800.0 (H)
U.S. Tungsten Reserves:		71.0

We are planning our consumption of electricity on the loose premise that nuclear energy will supply half our power needs in thirty years; without adequate tungsten, this simply cannot happen. The entire non-Communist world supply is only 321 thousand tons, not enough even for just American demand, and is only a third as much as will be needed by the non-Communist world (especially if there is wide development of nuclear technology). The total world supply, however, is 1,400 thousand tons. China alone has 1,007 thousand tons, three times more than the non-Communist world, which has only a fifteen- to twenty-year supply. China truly holds a very large trump card over the entire developed world in terms of this one resource alone.

Tin

Used in type metal, alloys, and, of course, to line steel cans (cans account for 95 percent of our tin consumption). Except for tiny amounts (by-products of other mining) there is no American production of tin because we have no tin resources and no tin potential. Most of the tin in the world is in Southeast Asia, but there is only enough to last mankind for thirty years.

		thousand tons
U.S. Tin Consumption:	1960—	80
	1980—	104
	2000—	165
		401 (H)
U.S. Cumulative Demand:		3000
U.S. Tin Reserves and Potential:		0.0

World tin reserves are 5000 thousand tons, of which the United States intends to consume over half by the century's end. It seems extravagant to be consuming nearly all of this important and scarce metal for tinned cans which just end up as unrecycled waste. When World War II cut us off from our Southeast Asian tin supplies, detinning plants opened in America and each housewife carefully cleaned and flattened her tin cans for recycling. Now there are no detinning plants at all, so 95 percent of our tin consumption is simply sheer waste.

A tripled or quadrupled GNP for 2000? Many of the minerals required are nowhere in sight and nearly all of the minerals that do exist are in other countries. If we triple consumption, the rest of the world will have to pay dearly. How will we get the tungsten we will need from China? We have severe electrical shortages now, and without tungsten for nuclear energy, we'll have even greater power shortages tomorrow because of the reliance our planning has put on this single power supply. It takes a lot of electricity to make aluminum, 10 kilowatts per pound, and we intend to increase aluminum production 14 to 30 times by the century's end. Without the necessary electricity, we won't be able to. If we can't make the aluminum, what becomes of the aircraft industry, among others, and hence the GNP? In view of the reality of supply, it isn't only ecological considerations which should urge us to lower consumption.

We must cut consumption because its future simply isn't there; if it were there, it would be an ecological disaster to consume it; and it would be immoral to gobble nonrenewable resources of hungry nations to satisfy our short-term dreams. Even if the vast majority of the human race avoids famine and dieback, it will never be able to develop if its mineral wealth has disappeared years before into American trash.

Future Fossils

As with minerals, any fossil fuel man will ever use exists today. True, oil, natural gas, and coal are renewable, but the time scale is in the millions of years, considerably beyond our resource planning. Our consumption pattern, however, sees an end to these vital resources —as with minerals, fossil-fuel consumption has grown at an astonishing exponential rate. Half the world's total consumption of petroleum occurred only during the last twelve years. Of fossil fuels in general, including coal, most of man's consumption took place during the last twenty-five years. The incredible acceleration of usage is expected to continue until the fossil fuels are completely gone.

Although we have known for some time of the very sizable *potential* oil supply tied up in shale rock formations in Colorado and other Western states, this is ignored here except where my sources have included it in total possible supply computations. As yet, we have no way to get the oil out of these rocks in commercially feasible amounts. Research, notably with nuclear power, is being done on a small scale. Perhaps in the future the shale formations will prove another Prudhoe Bay, but here we must consider only the oil we know we have or can believe we will find through conventional drilling.

Also as with minerals, the biggest—and most maddeningly unknown—factor in how long the resource will actually last is the uncertain ability of hungry supplier nations to industrialize. Once supplier nations can manufacture increasing amounts of their own goods, they will stop selling their natural resources. Although the situation for the majority of the hungry nations is so grim that their industrialization seems unlikely, it would be ghoulish to discount it and continue increasing our consumption. Although the depletion of fossils is charted for more distant dates than most other resources, they aren't expected to last so long that they won't be missed.

M. King Hubbard of the U.S. Geological Survey describes the rapid growth of population and industry based on rapidly increasing fossil-fuel consumption during the past 200 years as a growth aberration which will not continue, calling it "one of the most abnormal phases in human history." The era of fossil fuels is only a transitional period, from the prepetroleum past when change and growth were so slow as to be nonexistent by our century's standards, to a postpetroleum future when change and expansion will again be so slow as to be motionless compared to the rate we have known. That coming period of "nongrowth" may last forever.[18] Man, like the common bacteria, will have bloomed until all the nutrient was consumed.

We have several centuries of coal remaining and perhaps one century of oil, provided a great deal more is found and brought into production. Natural gas, used mainly for heating, is more short-lived. There is a deficit of about one-third in store for 2000, even if consumption of natural gas levels off during the 1980s as expected.

Natural gas and gas liquids are important raw materials for plastics and synthetics; this use is expected to increase

18. M. King Hubbard, *Resources and Man*, Committee on Resources and Man (San Francisco: W. H. Freeman, 1969), pp. 157–239.

five times during the same period. Burning the gas to produce electricity and to heat houses will diminish the supply until it falls below demand by the end of the century. The situation is similar to the former use of now-precious hardwood for fuel, although we can at least grow more hardwood.

Although tax structures such as the oil depletion allowance foster maximum domestic oil production, we've been a net importer of oil since 1948. Our greatest use is combustion, half of it by automobiles. There are 100 million motor vehicles today; they consume 80 billion gallons of petroleum each year. We expect to have 250 million in use in the year 2000, and will be making four times as many cars that year as this. It's imperative they do *not* burn petroleum.

Apart from poisoning us, petroleum combustion now generates carbon dioxide and water vapor at levels which will unbalance the climate, if continued, very likely before 2000. The ocean has generally been rising for the last 20,000 years—more than 2 percent in the past 80 years, and the trend won't be slowed by converting trillions of gallons of locked-away oil into water and icecap-endangering carbon dioxide. Should increased CO_2 cause only a few degrees increase in global climate by 2000, it could raise the ocean as much as 200 feet as the fringes of the polar caps shrink back. Certainly, our already shaken ecosystem will not be able to sustain even the non-Communist world's conversion of 46 trillion gallons of petroleum into water vapor, carbon dioxide and monoxide, and the sulphur and nitrogen oxides and acids, let alone the added smoke and heat.

Germane as this aspect of our planned consumption is to our continued future on earth, such enormous demand will rapidly run out of supply. We are expected to double our personal consumption by the end of the century until our cumulative demand by 2000 just about equals our *assumed* maximum reserves (these include huge unproven but indicated supplies). The authors of *Resources in America's Future* find it doubtful that even their medium U.S. demand figure can be met by domestic supplies despite a 20 percent import allowance.[19] Cumulative oil demand by the rest of the non-Communist world is estimated at 800 billion barrels (42 gallons each) by 2000. Add our cumulative import, and the demand becomes 850 billion barrels. As we will supply none of this, and cannot expect the Soviet bloc to contribute overly, the rest of the non-Communist world will have to get by with their 235 billion barrels of proven reserves, almost two-thirds short. Obviously, there will be a tremendous acceleration in exploration for new reserves to "develop." The situation in the Middle East, where over 60 percent of the current world's proven oil reserves are located, becomes critical to everyone.

Recent major finds, as in Prudhoe Bay and in coastal American waters, indicate that new supplies will continue to be discovered, but the cost to the environment of pumping oil from such novel niches is tremendous. It is doubtful that the tundra can survive its oil development. Arctic ecosystems, land and sea, are fragile and highly vulnerable to oil spills, which won't be broken down in the cold, but will remain for decades, clogging the food chain and raising temperatures as the oil-blackened water, land, and ice absorb more heat. The infamous Santa Barbara offshore disaster is only one in a series. A Nixon administration panel concluded that we haven't the means to handle large-scale oil spills, and

19. Landsberg, et al., *Resources*, p. 393.

that there will be a major pollution incident every year after 1980, when between 3,000 and 5,000 new offshore wells will be drilled annually. We have, however, already had more than one major pollution incident a year for the past several years.

After having caused immeasurable ecological alterations, the oil epoch will fall as rapidly as it rose. Oil production will shoot straight up (like population growth) until 2000, when it will begin falling rapidly. Figures presented by M. King Hubbard show world oil production in 2025 to be the same as it was in 1960. Barring dieback, there will be 15 billion people in 2025; there were only 3 billion in 1960. By 2075, oil production will have dropped to the 1925 level of one billion barrels. After that, it will drop almost immediately to zero.[20] There were 1.9 billion people in 1925, few of whom used oil. What do we have in mind for 2075? For if we increase our consumption to satisfy projections, the only market for a billion barrels of oil in 100 years may be rats, cockroaches, carp, and whatever other life forms survive us.

Water Resources: The Planned Famine

Americans entered the twentieth century as part of the one-third of humanity whose water was plentiful and safe; around the middle of the century, we joined the third whose water is uncertain in terms of safety and supply; now we are rapidly joining the last third, with dangerous and insufficient water.

20. Hubbard, *Resources and Man*, graph, p. 196.

Even though most of the water on earth is salt or ice, the hydrological cycle continually recycles 30 thousand cubic miles of fresh water across the planet's surface, a quarter of which is on the North American Continent. You'd think that 25 percent of all the fresh water on Earth would be more than enough for only 6 percent of Earth's people, but we have abused this resource to the extent that the Cleveland Fire Department must regularly hose down the Cuyahoga River or it catches fire. The Buffalo River has also caught fire in the past, and is a flowing fire and health hazard at all times. Every lake and stream in the nation is polluted to some extent —when the rain falls polluted from the sky, how can any stream be pure?

Of the 30 inches of water falling on America each year, 20 return into the air either through surface evaporation or plant transpiration, their version of exhalation. Eight inches of annual rainfall runs almost immediately back into the sea, but two inches sink into the earth to recharge groundwater supplies. Eventually, all the rainfall will return to the ocean for recycling, but lakes, ice, and groundwater delay the return; otherwise flash floods would punctuate constant drought.

As surface water sinks down to recharge groundwater, it is filtered free of most pollutants and has been, until recent times, a valuable supply of municipal drinking water. In some areas, one acre is enough to provide well water for a family, but in region after region, communities have found their groundwater so overloaded with pollutants that it cannot be used for drinking. Nitrate-poisoned groundwater is common in agricultural areas, and entire suburban communities have become crowded, septic-tank graveyards. The fouled groundwater also pollutes the lakes and streams it ultimately seeps into. Because of the fallacy that there is a part of earth which is totally incommunicado with the rest of the environment, we actually use groundwater to "dispose" of waste too toxic for surface dumping. We simply dig a deep well and pump the filth into it, as the Army did at the Rocky Mountain Arsenal when they injected 12 million gallons of nerve gas wastes deep into the earth. The waste lubricated rock strata causing slippage and earth tremors in nearby Denver. The Army is afraid to pump the waste back out; the sudden relief of pressure may cause a much larger quake. Meanwhile, the poison slowly spreads underground, to ultimately join the nerve gas in the ocean.

More alarming than its pollution is the actual disappearance of groundwater, whose natural seepage back to the ocean is usually balanced by fresh supplies from rain and snow. North America, however, is losing its groundwater twice as fast as it's being replaced; Europe three times as fast. Man is the disruptive element, paving vast tracts, 2 million acres a year in America alone, which shunt rainfall into sewers and rivers or trap it on the concrete and asphalt until it evaporates. Replacing forest and prairie with cropland reduces groundwater formerly held in the interwoven nets of root systems beneath the spongy humus of leaves. When it rains on cropland, or when crops are irrigated, little of the water is held in the soil; that which is not transpired by the crop usually evaporates, leaving a salt residue, or runs off, carrying valuable topsoil and silting harbors.

We also attack groundwater directly by pumping it up for municipal or agricultural use. Vast deposits of fossil water collected since the Pleistocene Era are being pumped up to irrigate Southwestern cotton fields; although this water has been stored fresh for over a million years, it will all have been returned to the ocean 15 years from now, after being spent to produce an inedible agricultural surplus in a desert.

Global loss of groundwater is a factor in the slow rise of the ocean's level, which has covered 2 percent more of the land mass during the past 80 years. We consume water by speeding rainfall to the sea, shortening or eliminating the period it is normally stored. As we intrude further into the planet's hydrological cycle to increase our water consumption, we will only be adding to the trend of the ocean's rise.

Many schemes are discussed for providing for the rising water consumption. One, the North American Water and Power Alliance, is a proposed "alliance" of Canada's watershed to the American Southwest by changing the course of major northward flowing Canadian river systems so water would be diverted from the Arctic Ocean and Hudson Bay through the Great Lakes and also down the spine of the Rocky Mountains ultimately through the Southwest and to Mexico. It would literally reverse the flow of much of the North American continent's watershed. The ecological implications are staggering, but the Canadians have yet to favor the "alliance" at all, let alone seriously consider selling their water.

Fully 200 times more fresh water is frozen in icecaps and glaciers than is liquid in Earth's rivers and lakes; the ice, like the groundwater, is a regulatory feature of the hydrological cycle, but plans are presented to artificially increase the melt of glaciers and even portions of icecaps to "hurry up" the supply of fresh water to industrially polluted or agriculturally depleted river systems. This is fine for those who profit from the "new" water as it flows past, but what happens as a major portion of the ice masses on land are gradually melted into the ocean? Aside from altering the solar heat balance by altering the total reflectivity of the planet, the vanished ice masses would no longer be pressing down upon land —rather, they would be added to the weight of the ocean. The Pacific Ocean, the world's major earthquake region, is ringed by fractures in Earth's crust caused by the weight imbalance between ocean and land; taking weight from the land and adding it to the ocean could lead to a geologic disaster.

The American consumer is the world's champion water user; a thousand pounds of water are needed to produce each pound of corn or sugar; 1,500 pounds for a pound of wheat; 10,000 pounds for a pound of cotton. A daily average American ration of 9 grams of meat requires using 1,400 gallons of water. Two eggs mean 80 gallons. Industry doesn't normally "consume" water since it returns it to Earth's system, but in view of how completely it poisons its billion gallons a day, we would be better off if manufacturers could consume it. When you trade your car in, you're trading the old model's 65,000 gallons of water pollution for a new model's 65,000 polluted gallons. A paper mill requires as much water as a city of 50,000 people, but can pollute it far more completely. The figures indicate that we face a water famine in ten short years.

Americans used 40 billion gallons of water each day in 1900, 525 gallons per capita. In 1960, we used 350 billion gallons a day—1,800 gallons per capita. By 1980, we expect to use 700 billion gallons a day—3,000 gallons per capita. By 2000, if we consume as planned, we'll need 1.5 *trillion* gallons a day—5,000 gallons per capita. Daily rainfall over America is put at about a trillion gallons, meaning we'll need all the rainfall in America *plus* an imported amount equal to the water used in 1900.

We're not expected to have 25 times as much water as was used in 1900, even with optimum engineering developments. This makes us 50 billion gallons short every day by 1980. As for the request for over a trillion gallons a day, it seems unlikely that we will even come close. It just isn't possible to usurp every raindrop everywhere.

As we splurge, we also waste appalling amounts of fresh water. Even while New York City waiters were forbidden to serve drinking water unless requested during the 1965 shortage, the city wasted through leaky pipes more water every day than the city of London used. London is slightly more populous than New York, but its water demand is only one-third.

We'll have to use a lot of secondhand water. In heavily urban areas of Europe and America, water passes through 10 to 40 pairs of kidneys before it reaches the sea. One in four Americans drinks water enriched with dirt and disease, and half of us drink water politely described by the government as "poor." Because germs and novel pollutants can't be removed by current nineteenth-century technology, Charles C. Johnson of the U.S. Public Health Service believes "illness and death could conceivably strike half the water-using population of one of our great metropolitan centers." Who comprises the nonwater-using population?

Water-borne disease is as ancient as civilization; cholera in Athens was described by Thucydides in 500 B.C. Cholera has spread alarmingly during the past thirty-five years until it recently has become an almost global pandemic, a constant source of death in much of Africa, Asia, the Middle East, the Soviet Union, and almost every region with primitive waste treatment and dense populations. A sixth of the human race is sickened by water-borne disease each year; 5 million infants die from water-borne disease annually, the same number of infants that die of starvation each year. Because cholera germs can reside latent and undetectable in humans and later be activated by emotional and physical stress, the disease can be carried from an infected region to any stressful city and there be triggered to contaminate an otherwise healthy population. We're not immune to cholera, and it's as close as the Connecticut, Hudson, Mississippi, or almost any other urban river.

Even if we stopped all water pollution, it would take decades for the lakes and rivers to cleanse themselves; the Hudson River and Lake Erie wouldn't be clean until well beyond 2000. As things are, the human race will probably never see these waters pure again. We've aged Lake Erie 15,000 years since World War II through artificial eutrophication.

Natural eutrophication usually takes thousands of years to convert a lake to a swamp and then to dry land, but biological death traps such as Erie are eutrophying thousands of times faster. As the mineral content of water gradually increases from the salts and mineral nutrients leached from the land, more and more algae grow, either as single cells or as long gummy strands. When the algae dies, its decomposition demands oxygen as does any organic waste (the term is Biological Oxygen Demand, or BOD; sewage has an extremely high BOD, as does most industrial waste). Oxgyen usurped by decaying waste cannot be used by fish and other animal life, and there is so little dissolved oxygen that the water will not support animal life—only the now booming algae population. The lake grows shallow, filling with organic refuse, its green water scummy and thick. Soon marshes and swamps surround it, year by year decreasing the size of the "lake" until the whole thing becomes a marsh and then dry land. About a third are being put through this process at such an accelerated rate that death of lakes will come in tens, not thousands, of years.

The Soap and Detergent Association, trying to throw a little controversy into the question of phosphate pollution, sponsored a study which concluded that carbon, not detergent-phosphate, was behind this sickening algae growth. Because all life is carbon-based, carbon is obviously required by algae, but this is rather like saying carbon is responsible for human overpopulation. Phosphorus is a natural plant control normally rare in water; plants cannot use carbon or anything else for growth unless the vital element phosphorus is also present. And only a small input will permit a large amount of plant growth, which is exactly why we add it to cropland. To claim phosphorus plays only a minor role in the "carbon problem" is highly misleading. There has *never* been anything but abundant carbon in the environment, but until detergents began adding the essential phosphorus, there was no problem such as exists today.

On the other hand, it would also be highly misleading to blame detergents alone for the problem, although they are a major and needless contributor. Human waste adds only a little less phosphorus to water than do detergents, and the phosphorus run-off from synthetically fertilized fields puts more of this nutrient into water than all the washing machines on Earth. All this when the staggering abundance of organic fertilizer, 1.5 billion tons of American animal manure a year, is also slushed into rivers and lakes. Crops treated with synthetic fertilizer require much more water than do those with organic fertilizer; the Great Lakes are at the lowest level in recorded history—Huron and Erie have dropped five feet in the last ten years—because much more feeder-water is diverted to Midwestern croplands. By shrinking lakes through eutrophication while usurping more of their feeder-water, as well as polluting groundwater with nitrates, synthetic fertilization is depleting our water resources.

Nuclear power generation creates 70 percent more waste heat than does fossil-fired; a nuclear reactor can require billions of gallons of water a day for cooling, and can return the water 50 degrees hotter than when it took it. A five-degree rise is enough to kill many species of fish outright and confuse mating and migratory patterns of other fish who assume the warm water means it's time to head upstream; it also causes fish eggs to hatch prematurely. Warm water increases algae growth and gives up its dissolved oxygen faster than cool water, thus furthering the contribution to the decrease of animal life and the increase of algae. When the water crisis is upon us in 1980, it's estimated that one-sixth the total stream flow in America will be needed for cooling reactors, and *all* the flow by 2000. Norman Brooks of the California Institute of Technology estimates that by 1980 some rivers could reach the boiling point and evaporate completely by 2010 as their water is heated again and again before it can reach the sea.

As we boil and shrink our water resources, we add 600 million pounds of pesticides, which kill tens of millions of fish annually, and industrial chemicals, 500,000 already in use and three more added every hour.

Why do we, who have more than anyone else, have

to run out of water at all? What manner of insane future planning is this? The AEC, however, assures us that we can consume as we will, and their reactors will provide our fresh water by desalting the sea to replace the fresh water their reactors have helped destroy. We aren't told what to do with the salt residues, scalding, concentrated brine as useful as billions of gallons of boiled-down urine: the ultimate resource of our water planning and the final product of our increased consumption.

Timber Trends: Shaving the Planet

"There is little forestry reserve in the United States today and the vast timberlands of Canada are facing exhaustion."   —A. P. Peck, Managing Editor,
                               Scientific American, January, 1944

"Through all the wonderful, eventful centuries since Christ's time—and long before that—God had cared for these trees, saved them from drought, disease, avalanches, and a thousand straining, leveling tempests and floods, but He cannot save them from fools."
                     —John Muir, founder of the Sierra Club

At one time America was the world's greatest temperate zone forest—800 million acres of diversified forest so dense and vast that early settlers believed it to be literally infinite. The destruction of the American forest is without parallel in the history of our devastation of our planet. Even when it became clear that the forest was limited, entire woods were cut not for agriculture, not for timber or fuel, but simply to provide a clear view. Lumbermen, for no purpose but vandalism, would not only cut every tree in a forest (clearcutting) but, when finished, would set fire to the ravaged acreage to ensure that nothing would regrow.

With one-third of the original world forest gone, there are not enough trees to serve the timber needs of today's population. Each year shows a net loss in world forest—and a net gain of 70 million forest consumers. The outlook for adequacy of forest resources until 2000 is by far the worst for any resource. The United States will see demand pass supply during the 1990s; this has already happened for most of the world.

On a world basis, there are 1.6 acres of forest per human being, according to figures presented by Georg Borgstrom in *Too Many*. Two-thirds of this is either marginal or inaccessible, reducing the amount of usable forest to about half an acre per person, but by no means so evenly distributed. Elections could not be held in a district in India recently because there was no paper for ballots. Excluding Latin America, the 62 percent of the human race which comprises the Third World must share only 5 percent of its pulp and paper—perhaps the chief reason world illiteracy is on the rise. Russia, with 7 percent of the world's population, uses 5 percent of its pulp. The United States, with only 6 percent of the population, uses 38 percent, which does not explain the rise of illiteracy here.

There is a myth at work which holds that we are self-sufficient in timber. True, North America provides us with 4.1 forest acres each, of which 3 are usable and accessible and 1.4 are actually being used. Americans, then, are supplying themselves with the produce of 1.4

forest acres per capita. Yet we import more wood than we cut—2 acres per capita to supply our outrageously wasteful paper consumption. Even so, America's forest is shrinking every year.[21]

According to the Forest Service, demand will pass supply in 1990; by 2000 our consumption of forest products will be 16 percent greater than our supply. Per capita use of most paper products is expected to at least double—including use of sanitary and tissue paper which is charted to rise from 26 pounds per person to more than 52 pounds each by 2000. As it is, the one-sixth of humanity riding first-class on spaceship Earth consumes six-sevenths of the world's timber products. One-third of humanity uses 90 percent of all pulpwood, with Americans at the very top of that third.

By 2000 Americans will be using enough lumber to each year make an inch-thick boardwalk 405-feet wide around the equator. Our plywood consumption that year will be the equivalent of a sheet three-eighths of an inch thick and 1,125 square miles in area. We could deck and roof the State of Rhode Island with lumber and plywood to be used in the year 2000, according to the Forest Service.

These 1,943,040 acres of wood that we plan on using —about the same area we currently pave each year—is enormous enough, but our planned pulpwood consumption is gargantuan. Our population is expected to increase only 70 percent during the next 30 years, but pulpwood consumption will more than double from 52.7 million tons in 1970 to more than 115 million tons. Perhaps a clearer way of looking at our paper and board use is per capita consumption over an eighty-year period:

21. Borgstrom, *Too Many*, p. 130.

1920—146 pounds per capita
1930—246 pounds
1970—507 pounds
2000—711 pounds

How will *you* use your extra 204 pounds? Not for books—book paper will not even double by 2000. The increase will be in packaging, tissue and sanitary, and other disposables, including throwaway sleeping bags!

We plan to use and throw away more than 18 billion cubic feet of pulpwood in 2000.

International Paper Company has been running a series of advertisements suggesting that through modern forestry practices—notably their own—we have such an infinite supply of paper that we should at once create what they term a "disposable environment." The irony in one recent ad is so fine I cannot help but quote:

THE STORY OF THE DISPOSABLE ENVIRONMENT

Tomorrow's baby may live in the same house you do. But he'll probably live in a totally different world from the one you live in. Because everything the baby wears or touches—virtually the entire environment in which he lives—can be disposable.

"Why do we need a disposable environment?"

The advertisement, eco-pornography if ever there was, goes on to explain that clothing, furniture, carpets, curtains, even whole houses, will be made of paper products and will be so amazingly inexpensive that we can simply toss them away when we tire of the color or the style or when the time comes to—horrors!—wash them. The ad concludes:

And by the time today's baby grows up, there's a good chance he may be moving into an entire paper world. . . .

The disposable environment—the kind of fresh thinking we bring to every problem. Nice to know it's at your disposal, isn't it?

International Paper Company, 220 East 42nd St., New York, New York 10017

Unless we "dispose" of their "fresh thinking" right away, there is only too good a chance that we *will* have *disposed* of the environment. What public relations such as this never seem to discuss is why, if there is so much wood, are the timber companies lobbying (and successfully) for a much bigger cut from publicly owned National Forests? Fully 72 percent of America's forest is in private ownership—paper companies own more of Maine, for instance, than do the people of the state. National Forests comprise less than one-fifth America's forest, yet they provide over one-third of each year's cut. National Forests are supposed to be managed on a sustained yield basis, which means that if a forest grows at a rate of one million board feet a year, no more than that growth can be cut. Yet because of pressure from the timber companies, the cut in National Forests has increased from 5 billion board feet in 1950 to 12 billion board feet today, a rate about 50 percent over sustained yield. Edward C. Crafts, Former Assistant Chief, Forest Service, recently told the House Committee on Agriculture:

"It is my feeling that the Forest Service has been and is being pushed close to the brink with respect to timber management on the National Forests. I do not believe in brinksmanship when it comes to depleting the natural resources of the United States."

What kind of management is it when 6 percent of the vast Tongass National Forest in Alaska is sold to U.S. Plywood-Champion for cutting and sale to Kanzaki Paper Mfg. Co. Ltd., of Japan? U.S. Plywood will receive $600 million for this wood and pulp—but as Dr. Edgar Wayburn of the Sierra Club contests, "the Forest Service is obligated to provide multiple uses of the national forests for U.S. citizens, not to provide pulp for Japan." This is the third time Alaskan National Forests have ended up in Japan, but this particular cutting—which will take up to a century to regrow—includes Admiralty Island, one of the few major nesting grounds remaining for the vanishing bald eagle.

But forests suffer considerable attrition from sources other than the buzz saw. Forest fires destroy about 10 thousand square miles each year, and air pollution is beginning to be recognized as a major hazard. Acid from smokestacks in Britain and possibly West Germany drifts to Norway and Sweden, where it rains and snows down on the Scandinavian forests. The sulphuric acid in the "black snow" dissolves minerals in the soil, altering its ecology in a way harmful to plant life. Calcium, for instance, is leached from the soil by the acid rain and washes into rivers and lakes where it further upsets the ecological balance of plant and animal life. Research in Finland has established a proportional relationship between mineral richness of the soil and forest growth. Dr. Eilif Dahl, a noted Norwegian botanist, has calculated that high acidity could reduce tree growth by as much as 5 percent a year.

Los Angeles smog is currently killing 150,000 acres of pine in the San Barnardino National Forest 60 miles away. On the East Coast, white pines have been similarly blighted, and pollution is thought to be a limiting factor in the growth of Canadian pine. Crops are also seriously damaged by pollution; like trees, crops can't stand the sulphuric acid from the oil and coal combustion which permeates their atmosphere. Bear in mind that there will be three times today's coal consumption in 1990 if nuclear power is in fullest use; otherwise far more coal will be burned. As other nations industrialize, world coal consumption will increase many times—as will the severity and global extent of forest-killing acidic rain.

Pine trees are also acutely sensitive to radiation—there are reports that great Canadian pine forests have already been stunted by fallout from bomb testing. China and France continue H-Bomb tests in the atmosphere. Radiation is released from many underground bomb tests. As nuclear reactors come to generate more of our power, they will further increase the over-all radiation level.

Forests provide many benefits other than paper plates and disposable diapers. Green matter converts carbon dioxide into oxygen. The carbon dioxide level is rising and the amount of oxygen in the atmosphere is falling. Oxygen is currently being consumed 1.6 times faster than it is being replaced, almost the depletion rate for our groundwater. Forests hold water in the humus they create, but when the forest is gone, the land erodes. We have already lost one-third of our topsoil to erosion, and each year we lose 117 million more tons of phosphorus, calcium, potash, nitrogen, sulphur, and other major elements to erosion. In 1882, a survey showed desert to cover one-tenth of the global land mass; by 1952, desert had grown to cover one-fourth the land; fully one-third the land is expected to be barren by 2000, and this tragic loss of arable land is due in large part to deforestation.

Forests undergo a type of evolution where one species of tree gradually succeeds another until the climax forest is reached; for example, a pine forest may gradually evolve into a forest of beech or hemlock. A forest still evolving is generally a more vigorous biological entity than a climax forest, more carbon dioxide is converted as more photosynthesis takes place. Nature has methods of slowing this succession; porcupines gnaw trees, as do beavers, insects blight them, fires ravage them. If man controls natural forest attrition, he can log the forest to the extent nature would have destroyed it and, if this is scientifically done, it can keep the forest biologically active. This is often the argument of loggers who claim that conservationists who seek to make forest lands "forever wild" are actually debilitating forest productivity. Although there is, in theory, validity to this point of view, in reality we do not practice over-all forest management to include sustained yield, which it must. We can control to an extent the attritions of nature, but we have not controlled the attritions of loggers—the history of our forests prove this, the projections for forest shortage indicate that this will be true in the future.

In this sense, forever wild is infinitely better than clearcutting, or overcutting, both of which are extensively done. A so-called stagnant climax forest is better than eroding acres of clearcut land. The battle is not, as loggers would like to have it appear, between "forever wild" and sustained yield, but between "forever wild" and "forever gone."

The Forest Service estimated in 1965 that we'd have to take 90 percent of the allowable cut from National Forests by 1980 and 100 percent by 2000. For the past few years the timber industry has demanded that the allowable cut be set at 100 percent. Their own holdings are largely overcut, and if we are to achieve a "disposable environment," the National Forests will simply have to provide it, and the Nixon administration so far seems to believe that public forests should provide private profits.

Imagine a solid block of wood a mile square and 60 stories high. This is our projected cut for 2000. Imagine another only 59 stories high—that was the cut for 1999. Imagine another block with no wood in it—this is what our planning has to say for 2001. The Forest Service, from whose projected data the above blocks are created, point out that their analysis can give no idea of the raw materials problems of the years after 2000, even though we know we will be 16 percent in the hole by then.

Resources in America's Future provides other data. Their medium projection for 32 billion cubic feet of wood to be consumed in 2000 makes the square-mile block 70 stories high; their high projection makes the huge monolith 122 stories. Although their medium projection indicates a cut of 32 billion cubic feet, they project there will only be 12 billion cubic feet growing stock. Our "sustained yield" will be running at a 20 billion cubic foot deficit—the cut will have to come from growing stock, which means there will be *nothing* for the future.

Resources actually projects an earlier demise for our growing timber stock than that. Most of our hardwood forests are in the East and privately owned. Of the original forest, only 10 percent is still in existence. Demand for hardwood will double by 2000 and will have to be met from growing stock as early as 1980. By 1999 there will be no growing stock at all for hardwood.[22]

Softwood grows primarily in Western forests owned mainly by the public; consequently, 60 percent of the

22. Landsberg, et al., *Resources*, pp. 355–369.

original forest is still left. Demand for softwood will more than double by 2000, but until 1980, most of the cut will come from older trees. After 1980 more of the cut will have to come from young trees, or growing stock. By 2000 there will be very little or, very likely, no growing stock remaining.

And this, remember, while we *already* import more wood than we cut. As with every other resource, world demand is going to increase sharply. Once gone, the forests will never return. They have not returned to Greece, Italy, China, Palestine, England, New Zealand, Mexico, Spain, Portugal, Libya, Turkey, India, France —the list is huge and growing. According to our governmental "planners," the list will include us in thirty years. According to the timber industry, with its delusions about disposable environments, it should, if possible, include us sooner.

International Paper has the largest hoard of privately owned forest in the world. Here is a statement of policy issued in 1968:

"The company will step up the harvest of timber from its own forest lands and begin to maximize profits by treating the land as current profit centers rather than as resource banks for future use."

It doesn't appear that they intend their "disposable environment" to last very long. Weyerhauser holds 3.4 million acres which it plans to exploit to a greater extent than ever by selling for commercial purposes. Georgia-Pacific fought against the Redwood National Park—Arcata Redwood Company is still fighting it. Japan, meanwhile, has increased her purchase of American timber by 2,500 percent in the past few years, and the figure is still soaring; we are in competition with Japan for our own National Forests.

We must not only immediately control our timber consumption, but also nationalize the remaining American forest.

The Continuing Energy Crisis

One of the most dramatic contests within the environmental crisis is the continuing energy crisis and the struggle between industry and conservationists as to how and with what shall America fuel her enormous energy consumption, 80 percent of mankind's total consumption.

Physical human labor contributes far less than one percent of the energy used in factories; energy use has been growing at 5 percent a year—nearly double the increase year to year of a decade ago. The Paley Commission in 1952 projected an electrical consumption figure for 1975 which was exceeded in 1968. According to the Commerce Department, "The U.S. per capita requirement for electrical energy has been increasing five times faster than population growth"; per capita oil consumption, 39 barrels in 1950, climbed to 49 barrels in 1965 and is expected to reach 69 barrels by 1980, "a gain twice as large as the growth in the 1950–65 period," according to the *Wall Street Journal*.[23] Just as with population growth and mineral depletion, we have consistently underrated our capacity to consume energy.

The United States holds one-fourth of the world's proven reserves of natural gas, and we believed this would fuel our consumption for twenty years; however, a more

23. October 5, 1970.

recent calculation shows that even if we stabilized gas consumption not to rise above today's levels, we would exhaust the proven reserves in only thirteen years. Economic studies by the Chase Manhattan Bank indicate that by 1980 the demand for natural gas will exceed supply by 50 percent: a shortage equivalent to 5 million barrels of oil daily. Natural gas provides 32 percent of our fuel.

American petroleum reserves comprise about 8 percent of world reserves, and according to Howard A. Baldwin, in an address to the National Association of Regulatory Utility Commissioners, our oil reserves "at the current usage rate have a life of less than ten years." [24] Oil gives us 45 percent of our total energy.

Coal provides 20 percent of our energy, and for the seventh year since 1960, demand exceeded production. In 1969, we were 25 million tons short, in the Federal Power Commission's estimate; in 1970 10 million tons; the deficit was made up from stockpiles. America has 40 percent of the world's known coal reserves, but much of it is at deep levels and in thin seams and will require shipping over greater distances than the easy-access coal we grew up using (and are currently exporting). Coal will have to supply an increased share of the projected over-all 56 percent increase in energy demand by 1980, clean air or not.

If we decide in favor of trying to clean the air, the *Wall Street Journal* reports an estimate by a Tennessee Valley Authority consultant that by 1990 the average home consumer will pay 25 percent of his electrical bill, or $80 a year, to remove only sulphur dioxide (this over and above paying, through increased prices, the $350 bil-

24. Reported in the *New York Times*, November 20, 1970.

lion required to expand electrical utilities to meet power demand by that time).[25]

Nuclear energy, which generates less than one percent of our power today, is still forecasted to provide 10 percent of our energy in 1980 (previous estimates had projected almost 18 percent), although public opposition to nuclear plants has so set the industry's calculation awry that even the 10 percent figure seems optimistic.

Sylvia Porter writes that we have actual shortages of supply:

We have left the age of cheap energy and entered a new phase in which prices of all forms of energy will climb steadily to new peaks. . . . Behind us is the time when comparatively stable prices of gas, electricity, oil and coal helped hold down our overall living costs. Ahead of us is a time in which soaring costs of these essentials will be adding to upward pressure on our cost of living.[26]

The affluent society, based as it was on exhaustible resources, has now drawn to a close. If we cannot control our consumption, we will not only have passed on to our children a society based on coal, climate imbalance, and air pollution, or nuclear energy and radiation pollution, but will be living in it ourselves in less than 20 years.

The energy industry (oil companies and electrical utilities) insist that the crisis can be forestalled to some degree if only conservationists would stop interfering. An all-out "development" includes perforating the continental shelves with off-shore rigs; immediate construction of the trans-Alaska pipeline; rapid increase of oil tankers; immediate wide application of nuclear energy, ready

25. October 5, 1970.
26. Reported in the New York *Post*, December 16, 1970.

or not; and rapid construction of various electrical facilities now tied up in court action brought by conservationists (such as the pumped-storage Storm King Plant in New York State).

The two-year ban on further offshore drilling has been lifted by the Nixon administration following Secretary Hickel's dismissal, and conservationists view with alarm the increasing incidence of major oil disasters from offshore wells now in existence.

The fuel crisis could be lessened if import quotas on foreign oil supplies were removed, although political developments in the Middle East have greatly lessened oil available from that area. Gasoline, furthermore, can be made from coal, as was done by wartime Germany; it's been alleged that the oil industry, which is moving toward monopolizing coal reserves, suppresses this technology in favor of more profitable conventional oil production. Although both suggestions would increase available fuel, it would hardly suffice. Even the vast fields of the Alaskan North Slope could not satisfy our demands beyond 1975, if that long.

We simply don't have it any more—we've already burned it.

Vehement as today's recriminations between environmentalists and industrialists are, the present ecological crisis is nothing like that to come.

The current surplus of oxygen in the atmosphere was accumulated over hundreds of millions of years ago during the Carboniferous Era, when young Earth was a vigorously photosynthesizing planet. The rich carbon dioxide atmosphere fostered plant life: like any exploding population, the plants finally depleted the once rich CO_2, polluting the remainder with their waste product, oxygen. Their numbers cut by depleted CO_2, plant life couldn't outgrow the teeming swarm of mammals spawning in the oxygen. Plant life has been losing its hold on the planet ever since the atmospheric balance turned against it. Man, who has so far shaved the earth of a third of its forest, seems on the verge of resurrecting the Carboniferous Era by exploding his population and waste.

These billions of years of carbon accumulation are the oil and coal whose final burning we have projected. As we undo what our vegetable precursors did, the atmosphere becomes richer in CO_2, warmer, and poorer in free oxygen; good for plants, increasingly difficult for mammals. Many ecologists warn that quickly reproducing billions of years worth of carbon dioxide will again tip atmospheric balance.

But at least the carbon dioxide will not scramble our genes or cause physical degeneration: it isn't radioactive. Because of an official policy which allots the Atomic Energy Commission 84 percent of all federal funds for energy research, we are prematurely committed to an unperfected and dangerous nuclear technology. We've pushed atomic energy at the expense of alternate sources of power; for example, we're an estimated five years behind Mexico in harnessing geothermal power.

Dr. Robert Rex, of the Institute of Geophysics and Planetary Physics of the University of California at Riverside, recently announced the discovery of a 4- to 6-billion acre-foot ocean of hot water beneath California's Imperial Valley. The giant steamfields, huge underground water deposits boiling at 500 degrees Fahrenheit, could be harnessed for $5 billion over the next 30 years and produce electricity equal to that of 15 Hoover Dams at maximum capacity, enough to obviate any need for atomic energy in all of Southern California until 2000 and potentially for centuries. The only by-product of such geothermal power generation, already used in Mexico, is distilled water—hardly a pollutant in a desert region. According to Dr. Rex's report to the Federal Bureau of Reclamation, tapping this huge power supply would take five to six years, but there are no "insurmountable technological or economic obstacles." [27]

Aside from geothermal, other power alternates include solar power, tidal power, magnetohydrodynamics (superheated gas), and fusion. Nonetheless, we're still concentrating our eggs in the fission basket. Senator Mike Gravel of Alaska wrote, in a letter to the *New York Times:* "It is unfortunate that we have an Atomic Energy Commission instead of an energy commission. A single word has condemned some intelligent public servants to a limited, radioactive vision." [28]

The only question we ask officially is how much hazard will we tolerate? Fission reaction leaks, so the AEC has set leakage standards of 41,400 curies a day (one curie equals the radiation equivalent of a gram of radium). The State of Minnesota was recently blocked by Northern States Power Company in trying to impose leakage restrictions of 860 curies daily. The industry claims there can be no fission at such low leakage, and the AEC agrees, siding with the utility against Minnesota and ten other states that joined Minnesota in the suit.

Dr. John Gofman of AEC's Lawrence Radiation Laboratory and professor of medical physics at Berkeley calls "an absolute, unmitigated lie" the statement that there is a threshold for radiation exposure below which no damage will occur.[29] Dr. Arthur Tamplin, also of Lawrence Laboratory, joins with Dr. Gofman in warning that when

27. Reported in the *New York Times*, August 6, 1970.
28. January 11, 1971.
29. Reported in *Newsweek*, February 16, 1970.

we reach the radiation dose permitted by the AEC, we will find ourselves with 32,000 more radiation-caused cancer deaths per year.[30] AEC policy is that benefits are to be balanced against such "costs." Nobel laureate Linus Pauling predicts mortality would be closer to 60,000 annually, not including unknown genetic damage which might remain dormant for generations or appear heavily in the first generation of the twenty-first century.

The defense of atomic energy stalls the development of alternate power sources. If you're interested in joining the energy debate, the Environmental Action Coalition lists the following for further information:

Committee to End Radiological Hazards
120 Christopher Street, Box 148
New York City 10014

Citizen's Committee for Radiation Control
340 East 51st Street, Room 14-D
New York City

Anti-Pollution League (nuclear)
92 Moore Avenue
Oceanside, Long Island, N.Y. 11572

Environment magazine recently reported that KMS Industries of Ann Arbor, Michigan, filed 9 patents—now being studied in secret by the AEC—which could, it is suggested, bring about the conversion of sea water to electricity within five years. Although fusion is usually projected for the end of the century, if it's clean, we need it now.

Even if we don't turn the Carboniferous Era loose, die of air or atomic pollution, or alter the construction of

30. *Ibid.*

human beings through radiation, Dr. James P. Lodge, Jr., chairman of the Colorado Air Pollution Control Commission, doubts that we could stand the heat of 8 to 10 times today's electricity:

In 30 years, at the present rate of growth, the energy generated and reaching the big metropolitan areas on the East Coast will be equal to that produced if you could turn on a switch and make the sun 33 percent brighter. . . . In 60 years . . . the thermo heat pollution will be capable of boiling to dryness the total flow of all streams, creeks and rivers in the U.S.

Should the progression continue for 200 years, the heat would equal what we now get from the sun but we would be extinct before that. Even producing the trillions of kilowatts for running the many extra small gadgets accumulating in our lifestyle will warm the ecosystem enough to produce unpredictable changes before the year 2000, especially in the densely populated Boston to Washington belt, where waste heat from power generation could approach half the total heat the area now receives from the sun.

In this instance, less power to the people!

Food: America's Anomaly

Our food trend is anomalous to the rest of mankind, and as it moves further into its apparent future of packaging and increasingly unintended as well as intended additives, what we eat and the way it's produced pose a growing menace to the common environment as well as to our nutrition and health. We have reached a point where pet food outsells baby food two to one and is the country's fastest-growing food product. Grotesquely, the wide variety of new types of high animal-protein pet foods provide many of the nation's estimated 30 million poor and hungry with the only animal protein they can afford.

On the whole, our trend is to the affluent "isolated eating" of billions of snacks and single-portion convenience foods. Over 5,000 new food products are introduced every year, ranging from breakfast cereals to gourmet concoctions. Not all succeed; 10 percent fail within a year, and many which remain will force others off the market. This high mortality is costly, but the development, design, and promotional costs are absorbed by the higher price for all food as a whole. The total consumer food spending each year must exceed money spent by the food industry, and of all money spent by the food industry, more than 99 percent is on advertising and packaging. A 1966 study by the National Commission on Food Marketing showed the following breakdown of that year's total spending by the U.S. food industry:

Advertising	$1,400,000,000
Package design	123,000,000
Food research	12,000,000
Total	1,535,000,000

According to the 1966 study, about half the price of a 40-cent box of breakfast cereal goes for advertising, packaging, and profits; only about 4 cents reflects the actual farm value of the cereal. Canned corn and tomatoes also cost more to package than they're worth; bread costs twice as much as its farm value. According to figures derived from the study's average market basket containing 17 basic items (no frozen or new convenience foods), the actual farm value of the food was only 41 percent of the final retail price. The target year for the study was 1964, and as the severe inflation of food prices since that year has occurred in every area *but* farm value, the gap between today's grocery bill and actual farm value of our milk, eggs, meat, vegetables, bread, and cereals is even greater today.

This gap is far greater with convenience foods, which embrace three categories: frozen food; food needing minimal preparation (boil-in-the-bag or freeze-dried items, for instance); and packaged food needing no preparation (puddings, toppings, gravies, snacks or single-portion products). Frozen food sales have grown 1,600 percent in twenty years, to an $8 billion market in 1970. Freeze-dried foods are only a few years old but already exceed 250 million pounds annually; similarly, the newly introduced boil-in-the-bag items now sell over 130 million pounds yearly. Columnist Sylvia Porter, who presented the above figures, cites the food industry prediction that of all the food products to be in 1984's supermarket, two-thirds have yet to be introduced. As this growth will be in convenience items, the cost of advertising and packaging will be tremendous and borne, of course, by consumers.

In 1940, the average American housewife spent five hours cooking her family's three meals; today she spends less than one hour, and in the near future will spend only minutes. Furthermore, feeding will be customized for each member of the family. The many thawable, boil-in-the-bag, heat-and-eat, freeze-dried, and add-water foods have already eroded the "family supper" routine in many homes—the final shattering of this tradition (which may be a factor in the decline of the family as a social unit) will be made possible by the microwave oven.

The microwave oven promises to be one of the most important modern sociological inventions, and a major amount of research and development for new food products is being conducted with it in mind. An entire meal can be customized of frozen, precooked, and uncooked-but-prearranged, units, locked into the radiation vault and served within minutes. Although there is still controversy regarding permitted radiation leakage, the Department of Health, Education, and Welfare is clearing individual models, and the sale of microwave ovens is expected to comprise 25 percent of the oven market by 1975, or a sale of 1.8 million a year. The era of the radar-baked 4-minute potato is upon us, and the vestiges of the family dinner may vanish as the kids learn to work the controls. The seep of radiation may, however, prove a high price for mother's convenience, especially to children growing up in the radioactive glow of these fascinating devices.

The tolerated radiation emission level is an economic compromise exceeding by 5 times the maximum level estimated by scientists to be safe; furthermore, the oven must be periodically inspected and adjusted to maintain emissions at even the controversial permitted levels. The radiation, a form of radar which permeates to rapidly cook meat, also damages human tissue.

If you must buy one, your most up-to-date source of information is doubtless either the latest issue of *Consumers Report* which tests microwave ovens, or the latest *Annual Buying Guide*, which is issued in December and covers much of the year's worth of product testing. A subscription to the magazine, or the *Annual* only, can be obtained by writing:

Consumer's Union
256 Washington Street
Mount Vernon, New York 10550

The magazine, as well as the *Annual*, is also available at major newsstands.

Essential to the "convenience" of today's food are some 3,000 chemicals used mainly to color, flavor, or embalm. Each of us eats about 3.5 pounds of these additives over the year, and we have but recently learned to question the hazard involved—many of the additives are now believed to be carcinogens, and new chemicals join the list faster than they can be tested. In 1955, we used a total of 419 million pounds of food additives; by 1975, we are projected to be using over a billion pounds, many of which have yet to appear.

Most of the eggs, meat, and poultry consumed in urban areas come from what are called "intensive," or "factory," farms. The entire trend in British and American animal husbandry has been toward sophistications of factory farming, which in essence is the combination of high-protein food, drugs, and such overcrowding that the animals' activity is close to nil.

"Broiler" chickens are raised by the thousands in gigantic, windowless sheds whose only illumination is from a few dim red bulbs. Should the light level rise above this eternal twilight, the chickens become aware of their condition and they begin to fight with one another. Many times the chickens must also be tranquilized and have their upper beak snapped off to keep their pecking down. Egg-layers spend their entire productive lives in cages so small that the bird can never open her wings; the floor is painful mesh, so droppings can fall through, and slanted, so eggs roll out to a conveyer belt. Food is similarly delivered by conveyer belt. The light is usually arranged to simulate a "new day" every 18 hours, which tricks the hen into spending the egg-productive part of her life more rapidly, and when it is over, she is killed and becomes the special at your supermarket.

Cattle spend the last months of their lives in feedlots so crowded that each animal has less space than the average bathroom. Veal calves must be white-fleshed to be of greatest "value." The whiteness is a consumer delusion, and is produced by a condition of acute anemia induced into the calf. The calves must be raised away from any stimulation and iron; they often "live" for their few weeks in dark stalls with their heads always held in yokes to keep them from licking nailheads around them, or even their own urine, and obtaining blood-reddening iron. Often, when the calves are removed from these stalls, they drop dead from the excitement of movement. This whiteness of flesh produces, of course, the finest, or more accurately, the most expensive, veal.

Pigs are among the most intelligent land animals; only the highest forms of primates, including man, score higher on tests. In nature, or even on the traditional farm, pigs play games, climb trees, fish and swim, and generally show a sense of "fun." In factory farms, they are raised in such overcrowded conditions that all the pigs in the "room" cannot lie down at once. Like chickens, they must be kept on tranquilizers in order not to develop hypertension, stress, and aggression.

Nature fights the intensive farmer vigorously with her diverse dieback mechanisms which ensure that no creature live in such ghettos except man. Calcutta is probably our only human parallel to a factory farm, but the tragic human beings there are not chronically drugged to suspend dieback. Factory animals are kept from being decimated by a dieback plague by eating meals laced with antibiotics. Often, the drugs are not enough, and entire indoor herds will suddenly sicken and die. Sweden and England will not buy our pork because of its high incidence of brucellosis and hog cholera.

Pigs are actually one of the cleanest animals; they have no sweat glands, however, and must protect themselves from heat by wetting their skin, if necessary, with mud. They are not dirty, lazy, or greedy; yet, they are a symbol for contempt. The reason for this is the same sinister one which for so long made us believe that black men were less than human, fit only for labor, and that American Indians were dirty, lazy, murderous, not to be trusted—fit only to be hunted down and their land taken. Indians, in fact, were listed as wildlife in a nineteenth-century catalogue of North American animals. We cannot exploit a creature unless first we debase it to "justify" ourselves.

Because of their affable nature, pigs are frequently pets on the few small farms which still raise them naturally. In ancient times, pigs were worshipped (it is believed to antedate the dietary code as the basic reason pigs are taboo as food in many religions). Pigs become so upset at seeing or hearing another pig killed that country people traditionally make sure to kill pigs only in isolation.

Pigs are born "housebroken," and the only reason for their undesirability as pets—their adult size—has been overcome by the Department of Agriculture, which has bred several types of miniature pigs, under 40 pounds when adult, primarily for drug and medical research (their organs and circulatory and nervous systems are remarkably similar to humans). An even smaller pig may now be available. Miniature swine would make excellent pets except that the USDA may resist if they feel the pigs' primary use in medical research would become protested. But these were developed with tax money and should be available to anyone who would like an intelligent, affectionate pet. For further information, contact:

> Genetics Investigations
> Swine Research Branch
> USDA Agricultural Research Service
> Animal Husbandry Research Division
> Beltsville, Maryland 20705

Your Senator or Congressman can help cut whatever red tape may be involved in buying a research animal from the government.

There is a fundamental immorality in raising pigs, or any animal, in conditions which are frequently so intolerable that only heavy drugging suspends sudden dieback. All life should at least have the chance, as much as its consciousness will allow, to experience sunlight and space to move, if not other joys of simply being alive. Perhaps the most detailed account of intensive farming is Ruth Harrison's *Animal Machines*. Rachel Carson, in her foreword, asks how far man can morally go with his domination over animals:

Has he the right, as in these examples, to reduce life to a bare existence that is scarely life at all? Has he the further right to terminate these wretched lives by means that are wantonly cruel? My own answer is an unequalified no. It is my belief that man will never be at peace with his own kind until he has recognised the Schweitzerian ethic that embraces decent consideration for all living creatures—a true reverence for life.[31]

31. Ruth Harrison, *Animal Machines* (New York: Ballantine, 1966).

Rachel Carson also finds it ecologically "inconceivable that healthy animals can be produced under the artificial and damaging conditions that prevail in these modern factory-like installations, where animals are grown and turned out like so many inanimate objects."

It has been this second awareness of potential health hazards, not "reverence for life," which is beginning to disturb consumers. Each year, the American livestock industry uses over 2.7 million pounds of antibiotics in animals. Antibiotic residues of over 300 units have been found in a single gram of beef; although this is higher than usual, many people have allergic reactions, sometimes fatal, to any exposure at all.

The most insidious danger in low-level antibiotic saturation is that germs develop resistance and the drug becomes useless medically. Apart from the possibility of immunizing virus in human systems, experiments by the British and most recently by the Food and Drug Administration, indicate that many of the germs that live in cattle stomachs, and which are constantly exposed to antibiotics until they develop resistance, can also infect humans. Although the British experiments have recommended suspending the use of antibiotics in animal feed, the FDA is still studying.

Antibiotics are used as growth stimulants as well as dieback fighters; another growth stimulant is diethylstilbestrol, a synthetic version of the hormone, estrogen. This is fed to 80 percent of our marketed cattle, in which it produces flesh gains of up to 15 percent. It also lingers as a residue in the flesh. Children are highly sensitive to estrogen; it can trigger puberty at an earlier age than normal, a phenomenon which is in fact observed in many of today's children. D-stilbestrol, put in pellet form into steer's ears, has been detected in the flesh of one of every

200 cattle slaughtered, and has, even at very low levels, caused cancer in mice. We are, as with pesticides, radiation, and many other major experiments upon our species, totally ignorant of what we may be doing with these drug residues in meat. But W. C. Heuper, former Chief of the Environmental Cancer Section, National Cancer Institute, is quoted by Ruth Winter in *Poisons in Your Food* as saying:

It is rather remarkable that biologically potent chemicals which are obtainable for medical reasons only on prescription by a licensed physician can be used freely in large quantities by persons without proper training concerning the potential health hazards associated with the handling and consumption of large quantities of these hormonal substances.[32]

To my knowledge, no study has yet been made of the potential effects of the wide distribution of these drugs in the waste from factory farms. These wastes are flushed into river systems already loaded with nearly every form of water-borne disease. Should the ongoing input of antibiotics into our septic rivers immunize the various germs already present, we could find ourselves in the position of not being able to fight the infections in our water.

The chemicals in our food also deceive us. Bread is not only embalmed for longer shelf life, but can be sprayed to actually smell "fresh." Sodium nicotinate produces the red illusion of blood-freshness in meat which, far from being fresh, may nearly be rotting: in this sense, a brownish cut containing no sodium nicotinate may be fresher than a bright red piece containing the deceiver. Sodium nitrate is also added to retard meat

32. Ruth Winter, *Poisons in Your Food* (New York: Crown, 1969), p. 48.

and fish spoilage. Processed foods can have the nutrition ground out of them during manufacture, and be later dyed and flavored to appeal to our senses. Often, some of the removed vitamins will be later replaced, but not all nutrition is put back even in the best cases. For one thing, not enough is known of the full complex of vitamins and minerals required for human health; "enriched" bread is actually synthetically rich in only a few limited areas, but is generally impoverished. The recent exposure of the low nutritive qualities of many breakfast cereals is another example of overprocessing of grains.

With our senses of smell, sight, and taste deceived by chemicals, we really cannot trust our basic guides to determine which food is good and which is bad. Instead, we must trust the motives of those who use the deception in the first place. There must be a point at which this becomes fraudulent; we don't buy food for its color, odor, taste, or even texture—these are only signals of its quality. We wouldn't tolerate a used-car salesman caught disguising the symptoms of breakdown and age in a used car, yet we pay for the same type of deception in our food.

Considering the added volume of packaging, the higher prices, and the chemical burden, one might wonder if modern food trends are more convenient for the manufacturer, distributor, and retailer than for the consumer. Ceil Dyer, in her *Back to Cooking Cookbook*, writes that the average housewife can save "an easy one-third" by avoiding convenience foods.[33] One of her examples is French dressing, 8 bottled ounces of which can cost up to 89 cents; with the finest imported olive oil, wine

33. Ceil Dyer, *Back to Cooking Cookbook* (Los Angeles: Price Stern Sloan, 1970).

vinegar, salt and pepper, a similar amount of dressing can be made fresh for under 25 cents. If you can buy quart containers of oil and vinegar you also spare the solid waste burden of six extra empty bottles.

Yet the trend is definitely toward increased convenience in our personal menu, and, secondly, toward more animal protein. To compound the anomaly, Dr. Hans Fisher, Chairman of the Department of Nutrition at Rutgers University, tells us that the cheaper foods are the healthiest and that the more expensive foods can actually be harmful. One of our food myths involves protein, especially animal protein: the more of it the better, we believe. The fact is that an adult should consume no more than two ounces of protein a day, although children require more, particularly when very young. It is much more difficult for our system to metabolize protein, rather than carbohydrates, into calories; protein conversion produces excessive wastes which overtax kidneys. Animal protein is particularly hard on the system, and if it is also high in cholesterol it may present added trouble.

Cholesterol is a tasteless, odorless fatty alcohol vital in body chemistry for making many important substances, including sex hormones. The body itself makes a certain amount, but it is also present in egg yolk, meat, and dairy products. It is linked with the build-up of fatty deposits in the arteries which reduce the flow of blood and eventually result in heart attack. The 1970 Intersociety for Heart Disease Resources, made up of 115 medical and nursing experts, recommends reducing the total cholesterol intake from diary and fatty meats and furthermore suggests that we cut our intake of saturated fats, those which are hard at room temperature (certain cheeses and so forth), in favor of liquid oils, such as polyunsaturated vegetable oils and, better, monounsaturated fats such as olive oil. The point is to lower the hard, saturated animal fats by reducing our protein intake from animals. If you are going to change your diet for these reasons, be sure to consult a physican to receive a detailed explanation of the diet change. It was conservatively estimated that changing the diet to reduce cholesterol in the blood by 10 to 15 percent could reduce heart attack risk by 30 percent.

Dr. George Reader, president of the American Geriatrics Society, wrote recently that vegetarians live longer, even if they become vegetarians after half a lifetime—apparently it's like giving up smoking: the sooner the better.

Dr. John Kellogg, health reformer and cornflake king, asked, "How can you eat anything that has eyes?" We must now include with eyes, antibiotics, tranquilizers, and hormones, as well as high pesticide residues. There were 4 million vegetarians in the United States in 1968; presumably the number is higher now with the recent concern over the uncertain qualities of meat.

Most people probably associate vegetarianism with an extremist point of view, believing it to forbid dairy and egg products, or to be unhealthy. There is certainly no need for us to become a vegetarian people; however, we can cut our excessive average portions of red meat in favor of lentils, soybeans, or any of the variety of other beans and legumes which are not only high in protein and inexpensive, but also require little lake-killing artificial fertilization because they "fix" their own nitrogen. Apart from the ubiquitous pesticide residues, these plant protein sources are free of the drug residues, sodium nitrate, and other chemicals added to meat purposely or accidentally. Meat generally has a higher pesticide residue than plants, but the pesticide in any case is usually the *only* such bonus in lentils or other plant protein.

As for remaining healthy with less animal protein, tests with college students have shown health to be maintained even on strict cereal diets, if supplemented by vitamins and minerals. It takes 7 grams of plant protein to produce one gram of meat protein; the average daily portion of meat alone requires 4.5 grams of primary protein; in total terms, we require as much primary protein just for our own feeding as does the entire hungry half of the human race. In terms of the contaminated environment which is concentrated in the food chain, we are doing the world and our own bodies no favor by putting so inordinate a personal protein consumption through so many food-chain conversions.

It would be needless and probably not entirely wise to overreact to the trend in excess animal protein consumption and convenience food use by shunning both. Animal protein is best balanced in its amino make-up (how the protein is "built") for human needs, and many convenience foods are really very sensible and, in some cases, less expensive. But our general American trend, for food as well as everything else, is to go much too far.

Protein Piracy

In spite of the Green Revolution's success in important areas, the United Nation's Food and Agricultural Organization reports per capita world food output dropped an over-all 2 percent in 1969, the first time in twelve years it has fallen. This condition, a reflection of rising population, is expected to continue. Although food production increased in some important areas such as the Far East, India, and probably China, it fell in the Near East, Latin America, and Africa. Total food production is estimated as an aggregate of pasture and cropland, forest, and ocean production. There was a slight increase in global farm production and a 2 percent increase in forest products (this means a reduction in total forest reserves); these gains were counterbalanced by a 3 percent decline in fishing. Not a decline in fishing *effort*—this is tremendously increased. The ominous truth is that despite the increased technological sophistication of fishing techniques, catches are not matching effort.

An example of what marine biologists warn is a global trend is the disappearance of sardines in France's Bay of Biscay. French fishermen have been "making up" for dwindling sardine catches in recent years by using finer nets, which take not only more fish, but more younger ones. The catch fell from 5,500 tons in 1956 to less than 1,000 tons in 1970. French fishermen are being ruined by their efficiency.

What is happening in the Bay of Biscay is beginning to be reported all over. Although biologists have been saying for twelve years that a sustained yield of anchovetes from the Humboldt Current cannot exceed 7 million metric tons annually, Peru has consistently overfished this area with diminishing returns each year. The resultant fishmeal equals the protein equivalent of twice the milk production of South America and is one and a half times greater than its meat production. The fishmeal is exported to the United States and Europe (as is most of the meat), which helps explain why Latin

America is down 2 percent in per capita food production.

The hungry nations now receive only 8 million metric tons of fish from the world's ocean each year. Considering that Peru alone pulled 12 million metric tons from the Humboldt Current in 1967, this is very little. But it is decreasing for the hungry nations as the global hunters move in with floating factories which freeze or can fish that formerly had to be salted for storage. Salted fish, less palatable to the affluent, went to the poor nations; the modern water-packed and frozen fish are more popular; thus, thanks to modern fishing technology, the hungry of the earth are getting less protein from the ocean.

The United States is the biggest importer of fish and shellfish. Tuna has always been popular in this country, but because of freezing or canning at sea, consumption of water-packed tuna is rapidly rising from the 2 pounds per capita of a few years ago. In all, we consume 65 percent of the world's canned tuna, importing 15 percent. Importation is rapidly rising. Check the cans of tuna in your supermarket and see how many brands are from Japan. The low price of tuna is deceptive; tuna stocks in both the Atlantic and Pacific are being overfished.

The British are alarmed at the diminishing Atlantic salmon stock; Americans on the West Coast and in Alaska are beginning to resent the fleets of Russian trawlers visible from shore, which overfish salmon migrating toward inland spawning waters. Koreans are sending fleets to Alaska; the Chinese are about to enter global fishing on a truly massive scale, perhaps to equal the Japanese and Soviets.

We are so often lulled with stories based on the limitless protein wealth of the ocean and how this source will feed the world and avert global famine. Yet we are already overtaxing this "unlimited" protein supply. This is not to mention poisoning it with pesticides, lead and carbon monoxide and mercury. The Baltic and Red seas are too contaminated for fishing, and even the otherwise clean waters of Canada and the deep mid-ocean produce mercury-poisoned fish. Most of the ocean is biologically very poor; the richest waters are usually near the coast, where rivers deliver the nutrient, and now the oil and poisons, from land to sea.

Even without contamination, the entire world catch would provide Americans with little more protein than we eat in red meat, according to Dr. Georg Borgstrom, who suggests that this is the true dimension on the "limitless protein" myth of the sea.

Professor Borgstrom, noting that protein is actually mankind's most valuable resource, suggests that in the near future it may become a major factor in world trade, much as gold is today, and foresees international protein banks.[34] We say that the minerals of the ocean, not yet exploitable, should be in common trust for mankind. Yet its proteins are considered fair game for any nation wealthy enough to compete. Dr. Borgstrom notes that white men have during the past 300 years moved into the pastures of other continents—Africa, South America, North America, Australia, areas in India and Asia—and either chased off, killed, or swindled the original inhabitants of their protein by trading empty calories for animal protein:

Seen in this perspective, the present large-scale exploitation of the oceans might be called our latest big

34. Georg Borgstrom, *The Environmental Crisis*, Harold W. Helfrich, Jr., ed. (New Haven: Yale, 1970), p. 83.

swindle. As Western white men, this time we are going out to the 'grasslands' of the oceans: the plankton pastures. We are mobilizing them, not to feed the hungry, not to feed the continents closest to these lush pastures, but to feed ourselves.[35]

We are frequently told of the *impending* world famine, but already between 10 and 20 million people every year starve to death. If this is not already a world famine, what do we have in mind for the future?

The problems of our anomalous food trend and our protein piracy are essentially matters of pattern and lifestyle, as is every other aspect of our diseased environment and moribund future. The global spread of our modern food trend would probably be the ruin of mankind. More than anyone else, it's the protein pirates in first class who are making the common vessel into a planetary *Titanic*; changing its, and our own, destiny depends mainly on our lifestyle.

35. *Ibid.*, p. 76.

Two: Making Ends Meet in the Gross National Product

The Eternal Depression

Economist Kenneth Boulding calls ours a "Cowboy Economy" in which both population and consumption must constantly expand in order to remain healthy. But while a new consumer arrives every 8 seconds, it is the rising level of per capita consumption which could make the dawn of the millennium the start of an eternal economic depression.

The Cowboy Economy was founded on the illusion of infinite resources, an illusion ended by the closing of the frontier a century ago. So the Cowboy switched to the illusion of renewable resources; if the range was fenced, it didn't matter how many head he ran over it— grass will grow back. But minerals don't renew, and neither can oil, water, timber, or soil when the depleting of them is constant and growing. A forest is renewable only if, after being selectively cut, it can be left alone to recover. We already cut more than we grow, so the forest is not renewable. Our intensively worked farm-land isn't renewable—it grows poorer at the rate of one percent a year. Food from the ocean is not renewable when whale and fish-breeding stocks are constantly over-fished by nations such as Peru, Russia, and Japan.

Even if the ocean stock weren't being seriously de-pleted, the poisons with which we are polluting the ocean may soon make the fish inedible. The pelicans along the California and Gulf Coasts are not renewable when the fish they eat contain 1,000 parts per million DDT. DDT slows or halts photosynthesis in ocean plankton, the food base for the entire ocean and the source of 70 percent of Earth's oxygen. We are still using DDT to grow cotton, and cotton and tobacco are our only agricultural sur-pluses. Even if we stopped using DDT, we still manufac-ture and sell it abroad. It doesn't matter who dumps the poison once it gets into the environment. Gasoline burn-ing (more in America than all the rest of the world) results in over 500,000 tons of lead raining into the ocean each year. Lead is normally one of the rarest elements in the ocean. How much longer will it be before fish will contain so much lead that they will be as inedible as the coastal shellfish are now because of industrial pollu-tion?

We are burning out the land, addicting it to high pro-duction based on synthetic fertilizers. Nitrogen, freely available in the air and essential to protein production, must first be modified to a form usable by the plant. Soil bacteria have done this for billions of years, but as soon as synthetically modified nitrogen is dumped on farmland, the soil bacteria mysteriously stop working. This is addiction in the truest sense: once introduced, it must not only be continued thereafter, but each fix must be greater than those previous in order to achieve the same result. By 2000 we will be using yearly, on a world-wide basis, synthetic fertilizer which will weigh more than the entire human race at that time. The ecological effect this will have is fantastic; no longer will we speak of ponds and lakes eutrophying—we will worry about the sea itself.

The Cowboy Economy is burying us beneath 8 million junked cars, 76 million disposable containers, 30 million tons of wastepaper, tens of millions of tons of industrial wastes and raw human sewage, plus 3 pounds of pesticide and one ton of smoke and fumes for each American citizen every year. Senator Gaylord Nelson maintains that this destruction of our heritage and debasement of our lives is the antithesis of freedom. He proposed a Constitutional amendment:

"Every person has the inalienable right to a decent environment. The United States and every state shall guarantee this right." [1]

Yet this decent environment cannot really be legislated, even if it could be exactly defined. The pending eternal depression was created by millions of individuals, and if it is going to be avoided, millions of individuals will have to do it. Yet we should have this amendment as a base upon which to start. The closest we came was the National Environmental Policy Act of 1969; now being tested in eighteen pending court actions, the act would have made a decent environment a constitutional right, but a House-Senate Conference Committee removed this stronger "set in concrete" protection in favor of making a decent environment "national policy." Senator Nelson warns that by 1980 people in many regions of the country may have to wear breathing helmets outdoors. Dr. S.

1. Gaylord Nelson, *Look*, April 21, 1970, p. 33.

Dillon Ripley, secretary of the Smithsonian Institution, believes that between 75 and 80 percent of all remaining species will be extinct in 25 years. If this happens, the human race will be finished as well because the planet's life support is based on the diversity of life forms. Simplifying the ecosystem by reducing this diversity will assure collapse.[2]

The processes for this massive potential extinction are well established. Billions pounds of DDT in the atmosphere have yet to descend and finish the damage we have seen begun. Thousands of tons of DDT in the Antarctic icecap will be released as it slowly melts and sloughs into the ocean. Senator Nelson's amendment can do nothing about this, just as it cannot unpave the 2 million acres we lose to asphalt and concrete or the 5 million acres we lose beneath suburban sprawl each year. Perhaps if his amendment led to a national policy for land management we would not remove those 7 million acres from wildlife habitat each year. Perhaps we could halt the nationwide use of mercury as a seed dressing and, keeping this poison out of our game birds, stall their extinction. Perhaps we could curb the timber barons and thus preserve the required privacy for the bald eagle, the wolf, the bear and elk and mountain lion and other desperate creatures. And perhaps we can come up with a less-than-lethal form of personal transportation.

But the real problem of the Cowboy was not created by law. The real problem is the style of our lives.

Changing our lifestyle will involve the greatest willful cultural transformation in the history of civilization. Certainly, it will include rethinking or dumping the Judeo-Christian ethic which has man dominating nature, an

2. S. Dillon Ripley, quoted by Gaylord Nelson, *ibid.*

attitude integral to our scientific arrogance toward natural systems. Perhaps it is time we recycle the ancient worship of the sacred grove.

Our basic concept of science will have to change, and is already beginning to: we know we cannot pull reality to pieces and study the physical, chemical, biological, and philosophical fragments out of context. Only 100 years old, the integrated concept of ecology is beginning to seep throughout science and society. We should be teaching ecological concepts in day-care centers.

The concept of synergy within biological systems must be at the base of our actions and outlook or ecological disasters such as the Crown of Thorns infestation and the Australian Mouse Plague will become commonplace. Old-fashioned living rooms often still have the Triton shell, that large, pearly seashell in which one can listen to the "ocean." Triton shells in doileyed American parlors reduced their number in tropical Pacific waters; DDT and other chemicals may have further decimated them. At any rate, they can no longer control their chief prey—the Crown of Thorns starfish. The Crown of Thorns is exploding in number, consuming coral from around Pacific atolls. Over a hundred square miles of the Great Barrier Reef have been eaten away and the entire formation is endangered. When it goes, ports on Australia's east coast will be unprotected from the ravages of the open Pacific. Ninety percent of the atoll surrounding Guam is being eaten by the starfish; without the protective ring of coral, Guam and other atolls will be eroded by the ocean. As the Crown of Thorn starfish is free-swimming in its larval stage, ecologists fear it will swim through the proposed sea level Panama Canal and establish itself in the Caribbean, destroying beautiful coral formations there, too. The smallest coral atoll is larger than anything man has ever built; the largest atoll is greater than the sum of man's structures on earth today, and possibly throughout history. Ecologists fear that poisonous Pacific sea snakes will swim through the sea level canal to threaten Atlantic fish species not adapted to them. The deadly snakes may also endanger human swimmers at Caribbean resort beaches.

Because man has so simplified Australian ecology in attempts to produce food, there are now periodic plagues of mice—300 million on one occasion—which suddenly swarm through towns and fields, destroying everything. Highway traffic is impossible because of vehicles skidding on crushed mice; poisoning them is no good because they crawl away by the hundreds in every house and die in inaccessible places, causing not only stench but disease. Cats were brought in, but killed so many they quickly lost interest long before they could make even a minor dent in the population. Such plagues also occur yearly in Middle Europe.

Giant African snails crawl over portions of Florida, eating not only vegetation but also house paint. The foot-long snails were carried around the world by sailors as a "novelty" and, away from their predators, continue growing uncontrolled in many parts of the world.

The Antarctic fin whale is another example of our failure to perceive synergy in nature. Biologists warn that the fin whale, like all whales, has been so greedily slaughtered that the few that remain may not be able to survive the natural attrition of their environment. Man may have failed to grasp the concept of a population threshold below which extinction is inevitable, but the fin whale seems to understand; twenty years ago, they didn't become sexually mature until eleven or twelve years of age; no longer able to afford a long adolescence, they now mate at age six. An entire species changes basic behavior in an attempt to survive, yet we consider ourselves to be in the Creator's image.

Changing our basic religious, scientific, and philosophic attitudes will take a long time. Our environment may not last out our own generation. What is most urgently required of our generation is an environmental holding action while we educate our children.

Until we can bring about a national resource-depletion freeze, we should institute individual freezes. For example, careful selection of foods and consumer goods can save up to half of our indirect water consumption, and we can halve our direct water consumption as well. It isn't necessary to go without drinking or to stop eating interesting food or buying useful products; if we just avoid the excesses, we will go a long way to assuring that we have no water famine in 1980.

If we grasp the concepts of integration and synergy and apply them to our individual lifestyle, we will be acting in the only workable way to avoid the disaster of an eternal depression by 2000. The alternate is the continued rapid disintegration of life support, a dieback or two before the end of industrial civilization, and—if we fall below the species survival threshold the way we've driven blue whales to do—the end of man himself.

De-advertising the Gross National Product

Kenneth Boulding views the concept of a Gross National Product as a social invention which changed life as much as any mechanical or electronic development. GNP is a dollar thermometer that must always rise and, whenever we use it or any other abstract symbolic scale, we rapidly become confused as to whether we are measuring something or trying to make it adjust to the scale

We aren't really sure what GNP is—of just *what* is it the scale for measurement. It isn't the total cash value of all material products, as the name suggests. GNP includes tangibles such as number of locomotives, but also intangible services and the price of Vietnamese war. Dr. Boulding uses pollution as an example of GNP ambiguity: a reeking dead lake may degrade its community for years, but this is not counted off GNP; the price of cleaning the lake would, however, increase GNP.[3]

Pollution is a positive input to GNP—it's literally a market for cleaning up. Pollution control, in fact, is expected to be a $25 billion a year industry in a few years. The GNP also sees emphysema as not negative (except for unemployment) to the economy and positive to GNP when you buy a respirator. The GNP doesn't consider depreciation—certainly not ecological depreciation—yet consider how much the landscape has depreciated since 1492 because of the Cowboy's "improvements" via higher GNP.

Because Gross National Product doesn't actually indicate what we *have*, but rather what we've had to consume to stay even or, hopefully, get a little ahead of last year, Dr. Boulding suggests the economic concept be more truly named Gross National Cost, and that we become increasingly alarmed as it rises. But we boast of higher

3. Kenneth Boulding, *The Environmental Crisis*, pp. 157, 170.

GNP. We cannot accelerate depletion of resources or simplification of biota to cure our present economic problems the way we cured the Great Depression. There was an excuse then—World War II—but when the war ended, perhaps we were afraid of falling back into the 1930s if production returned to prewar levels. Rather than diverting the stimulated production to the social rebuilding of America, it went the easiest and most profitable route: into consumer goods. This Gross National Cost can't continue as a depression dodge because it isn't a dodge at all, only a play for time by the manufacturing generation which intends on surviving about as long as the raw materials: A.D. 2000.

Dr. Preston Cloud, professor of biogeology at the University of California, Santa Barbara, predicts that mankind will be out of natural gas, zinc, tin, gold, silver, and platinum in twenty years; out of uranium and copper in less than a hundred years. As we have seen, the shortages are in many cases closer than that. Iron and coal, which should last for centuries, will deplete much sooner, as they must increasingly replace other metals and fuels that run out before them. Dr. Cloud suggests that within our lifetime, cars will become rare, even pots and pans will be luxury items, and we will have difficulty finding expensive fuel to heat our homes as the fossils fade: "We are relying on scientific discoveries which have not yet been made to bail us out in time, there is no guarantee that they will be made in time. We are already at the point where we need them." [4]

We are said to have reached the trillion-dollar GNP because of inflation rather than actual economic growth, at 12:02 P.M., December 16, 1970, a "growth" rate of

4. Preston Cloud, *Resources and Man*, pp. 135–154.

$2,000 a second. Yet real growth has not occurred fo
over a year; in terms of actual growth, GNP fell 3.3 per
cent in 1970. Is the GNP clock rigged to run back
wards as the resources deplete? Such abstractions a
clocked national wealth tell us nothing of the future, ex
cept the rate at which it is being consumed.

It may be too late to change the trend; the remainin
biota and minerals are not only being depleted by u
but by people far more desperately in need of them, an
we may not enjoy the competition when we start losin
In the near future, we will be in a hot business war wit
Japan, the second largest, and fastest-growing, economi
power on earth. The Japanese are projected to equal an
probably pass us by 2000 in terms of global economi
clout; they already have a vast global business empire t
which they devote as much energy as we do to our fa
less productive global military presence. The ultimat
depletion of resources could be more the result of th
Japanese business empire than of American consumptio
even if we can moderate our demand, it seems question
able that we could persuade Japan to similarly "cool it
After all, we forced western technology into Japan be
hind Commodore Matthew Perry's cannon.

GNP and waste have been rising at an annual rate
4 percent each, certainly no coincidence. Mechanize
farming brings forth more bushels per acre, but co
sumes more calories than are delivered. The world
short of phosphorus, but it's killing a third of our lake
similarly, there is a global shortage of sulphur, yet w
vent as much sulphur into the air as we mine each yea
and the sulphurous rain ruins forests in the industrialize
sections of the Northern Hemisphere.

We face a national power shortage, and even if w
turned immediately to a 100 percent nuclear-fired gener

tion, uranium supplies would suffice only until 1980. Yet the utility monopolies encourage the large users to consume more by structuring their rates to fall off with increased consumption.

Although said of damage done to soil microbiology by intensive agriculture, Professor LaMont C. Cole's comment, "What is now popularly known as progress begins to look very much like the path to extinction" applies to the advertised consumer society as a whole.[5] Advertising is rampant for wild-fur coats, redwood paneling and patio furniture, new disposable paper goods, nondegradable aluminum and plastic packaging, small electrical "time-savers," and unnecessary "hygiene" products.

Although soap advertising is massive (Proctor & Gamble, at $260 million for 1970's ads, is the nation's largest promoter), an ad campaign over fifty years old is directly tied to today's pollution. Before World War I, soaps didn't stress suds in their claims; suds have no cleaning value, they're only a visible by-product. But some enterprising copywriter capitalized on the apparent connection between suds and cleaning power. Soap began to advertise on the basis of rich suds; the trend established itself in the 1920s and stayed with us until synthetic detergents were introduced just after World War II. The detergents didn't make suds and because of this didn't sell. The manufacturers added artificial sudsing agents— and detergents began selling. Then, during the 1960s, disquieting heads developed on rivers and lakes, so bad that they halted navigation on some major rivers. The detergent, suds and all, wasn't biodegradable and couldn't be handled by sewage plants or natural digestion. Threatened government action brought about a complete re-

5. LaMont C. Cole, *The Environmental Crisis*, p. 10.

formulation of detergents; now all detergents are bio-degradable: phosphates were substituted for previous "hard" chemicals, such as the artificial sudsers.

Advertising is much more successful than education in terms of shaping our culture. If we've learned anything unique as a people, it's how to smoke. Try teaching that in a classroom with a dull textbook. We've learned to not want public transportation, but a fragmented "system" of cars—not just cars: muscle cars. Try convincing a sensible, 80 percent urban population to behave this way by means of a university night-school course. Any evaluation of GNP and controlling the consumption-depletion-pollution syndrome must consider advertising as a prime energy imput: it moves the entire operation as clearly and as basically as sunlight moves the air and water cycles. If we are going to make something of our GNP other than the indicator of how fast the environment is disintegrating, we'll have to somehow control this energy input.

This is by no means to advocate a ban on commercial advertising, but to suggest that a "fairness" doctrine be applied similar to the FCC regulation that smoking ads, before they were removed, had to be countered on television by anti-smoking ads. Signs of increased control over advertising are indicated in the pending Federal Trade Commission case against the Coca-Cola Company for advertising their High-C as higher in vitamin content than natural fruit juices. If the judgment is for the FTC, Coca-Cola may have to state in future ads the previous deception, and they may lose the brand name.

And might not there also be advertising in the public interest informing us that increased consumption makes us poorer, not richer? Certainly, it's only fair. In view of the facts of resource depletion, advertments for disposable paper products, needlessly powerful automobiles, and other consumer excesses should be recognized as "controversial."

Advertising, the only effective means of behavior control ever evolved for media communications, could prove a very powerful positive force. We are otherwise very slow to change. A catastrophic brush fire devasted regions in southern California in 1970; these fires occur about every five years and are somewhat predictable. Builders nevertheless put developments in highly flammable chapparal and use flammable materials, such as shingle roofs. Many victims of the recent fire will rebuild in the same area and with the same materials. The same holds true for the mudslides of a few years back. A few decades ago, earthquakes rocked California, but rebuilding covered the fault lines. Early in 1971, Los Angeles was torn by a tragic earthquake, yet rebuilding once more seems to assume that the land will never move again. Every year, in fact, we construct $10 billion worth of urban buildings on potential earthquake land, according to the U.S. Geological Survey. The recent cyclone and flood in East Pakistan, one of the worst disasters in man's history, is a perfect example of how men don't allow reason to guide their behavior. The East Pakistanian delta is hit by a cyclone or tidal wave every three or four years. A study conducted there a year before the disaster showed 40 percent of the people to have lost all of their property to previous floods. Even when the tidal wave slowly began rising, people just climbed on chairs, beds, rafters, then roofs. Although it rose slowly, the water came up 20 feet. Most of the 300,000 to 500,000 estimated dead had more warning than most natural catastrophes allow. We've had the warning about DDT for nearly ten years and it is still in agricultural use, and proposed restrictions for other harmful farm pesticides have quietly been canceled.

Many people starve to death needlessly each year because of their inflexible behavior patterns, which prevent them from eating available wheat and corn instead of their usual, but scarce, rice. If this inability to change seems extreme, consider what habit patterns have done to New York City. Or consider the sewer system of any city proud enough to have one. Modern sewers are really Victorian and, in some cases, Ancient Egyptian technology repeated and made bigger by extension. They don't do their job because of our habituation to the notion that human and kitchen waste should go into millions of tiny leaky pipes which join into larger pipes which are sometimes filtered before entering the river. The idea was all right when cities and their sewage output were small enough for this system to be workable. We stayed with it through habit, however, and it is now hyper-complex and unworkable. Habit still has us committing what billions we hope to raise for bettering the treatment plants, but even billions of gallons of "better" sewage have no place in a river. This is like replacing the crank with an electric motor in the design of a clockwork TV set: if the basic concept is outmoded or inappropriate, efficiency at one end won't make it work.

Gladwin Hill writes in the *New York Times*: "This propensity of people to adhere to life patterns that invite trouble is recognized by ecologists as perhaps the most perplexing and ubiquitous factor in the 'environmental crisis.' " [6]

The drive to consume is one of the pathological hallmarks of our society; and advertising plays a key role by

6. September 30, 1970.

reinforcing the pleasure of *buying*, but not of actually *owning*. One has to keep buying soap anyway, so the effect isn't as noticeable with soap or other products which are used up. But with major appliances, television sets, cars, and so forth, the effect is very noticeable. A Volkswagen owner gets purchase confirmation from Volkswagen ads for years because the product changes so slowly—in this instance, he is reinforced to own. After a few years with his Buick or Mercury, however, the owner stops getting such positive reinforcement from the ads; with each year's planned obsolescence the ads become more negatively reinforcing until that magic moment when psychology and mechanical breakdown combine, resulting in a new car purchase. This particular consumption behavior, so vital to our GNP, is very carefully planned.

High consumption habits will have to change. There's a factor, usually called the Green Revolution, which, if it works, will not only force this change sooner than we think, but also alter the entire ecological, political, and economic balance of the world. We think that by promoting the Green Revolution we are mainly attempting to feed hungry nations. If we succeed, the side effects will be gigantic.

The United States maintains one-third of the world's industrial production. The chief reason we do is that our Green Revolution started about a hundred years ago. Very simply, the Green Revolution is modern agriculture: high mechanization, large crops of a single species bred for high yield, heavy artificial fertilization, heavy and frequent use of pesticides, and copious irrigation. This parlay finally started paying off for us during World War II when manpower shortages and high food demand forced massive new agricultural methods into use. We maintained those high production levels after the war, resulting in the well-advertised food surpluses of the 1950s —which many people think we still have. The effect of our Green Revolution was to release so many people from food production that America is now 95 percent industrial and 5 percent agricultural.

Today one farmer and his machines and chemicals can feed forty other Americans who must then become factory workers, repairmen, salesmen, hairdressers, and so on. Food is so cheaply produced that we spend only 18 percent of our budget on it, the lowest in the world. Japan spends 38 percent of its income on food; people in hungry nations spend much more, up to 100 percent. Were it not for our Green Revolution, we could not be generating one-third the world's industrial output. As it takes a majority of manpower to produce and a majority of income to buy food in underdeveloped countries, they must remain agrarian and underdeveloped. If developed, their natural resources now sold to the manufacturing nations would be used for their own industrialization.

If the global Green Revolution works (many ecologists say it will not), it will release vast populations from the field, just as in America. The only way a nation will be able to absorb these millions will be through industrial employment—it will be forced to industrialize if only to prevent chaos. The consumer surge will be terrific in every nation where a Green Revolution works. Our Revolution has taken a hundred years, yet like so many other long-term developments, it can be leapfrogged onto another nation within five years.

Now, industrialization requires huge capital, which hungry nations are notably short of, and this will produce a lag, but this will be only a delay. They will probably get it from some rich nation. Japan spends a surprising amount on foreign aid, mostly attached to business deals; they are about to commit one percent of their GNP to foreign aid—a *far* greater amount than we spend. If the Green Revolution works, the main result as far as we personally will be concerned will be a diversion of our sources of raw materials.

As this diversion automatically means higher prices and lowered consumption, perhaps it is best we begin preparing. We have begun to de-advertise cigarettes and products with false claims; we should either begin to de-advertise the GNP or else cynically support a Brown Counterrevolution, the precedent and logistics for which are already established in our massive defoliation of Southeast Asia. Many ecologists fear the permanent effects of our war against cropland; it may be many years before we have to worry about the defoliated nations achieving the position where they could deny us their raw materials because they'd be able to stand on their own feet agriculturally and begin industrialization.

If we could extend our defoliation programs to other hungry nations, rather than exporting Green Revolution, we could perhaps continue our national maleducation through consumer advertising and maintain our one-way, no-deposit no-return GNP for twenty or thirty years. Otherwise, de-advertising our Gross National Product may be necessary for our survival sooner than we think.

Reusable Rose

If our GNP is raw material on one end, garbage on the other, recycling is the science of making ends meet.

Many consumers show resistance to recycling programs which will affect them intimately; for example, many don't relish the prospect of eating bread baked from the slime grown on sewage, but if the sewage were fortified with calcium, lime, and other nutritive essentials and used as field fertilizer, bread grown from the wheat would probably be acceptable. The nutrient goes through a green-plant conversion in each case, but wheat flour appeals more than algae. There is a problem insofar as the sewage would have to be sterilized; if gamma rays were used, care would have to be taken regarding radioactivity. Still, much reluctance seems psychological rather than biological or chemical: a feeling that the only decent place for sewage is out of sight.

Another and far more silly impediment to recycling is a culturally acquired behavior whose reinforcement if not origin can be attributed to advertising—the notion that the truly affluent do not reuse things or bother to repair minor tools and appliances. Our time is too valuable to waste in maintenance and cleaning when for only "a few cents more" we can discard. Discard and *replace*, of course. During the depressed 1930s and the war years following, containers were saved and reused or returned. During the war, housewives routinely cut both ends from tin cans, flattened them, and tossed them in the box for the metal drive. After the war, more and more disposable packages were introduced. Packaging is today a $29 billion-a-year industry. The average returnable beer bottle was once used thirty times; now it is used only nineteen times. A few years ago, Pepsi-Cola put 14.4 million returnable quart bottles in circulation in New York. At 5 cents each, the bottles were worth $720,000, but after six months none were coming back to the bottling plant.

Naturally, industries dependent upon noncyclical products present a resistance to recycling more easily understood than psychological or cultural consumer patterns. With the competition from metal cans, the glass industry feels enforcement of 100 percent returnables would be an economic disaster for them and would only increase the number of cans. It's plain what would happen to the paper and plastic industry if milk suddenly came in returnable glass bottles again. Eliminate disposable glass jars and the awesome factor of plastics, especially polyvinyl chloride (PVC), is increased. But regulating all the industries simultaneously would be a major—and in the present structure of government agencies and lobbies probably an impossible—political feat.

Some industries resist recycling because it is still cheaper to obtain some materials "raw." This type of "economy," practiced by the steel industry, for example, is a short-lived illusion subsidized by importation and depletion. Secondary (or recycled) materials account for large amounts of our nonferrous metal supply. Thus, 20 percent of our zinc, 30 percent of our aluminum, 45 percent of our copper and brass, and 52 percent of our lead come from secondary material. Perversely enough, not only are no government incentives offered the secondary material industries, but it is often hindered by zoning and other regulations. Even so, millions of tons of solid waste were returned in 1970 as $7 billion worth of resources.

With help, this vital industry could become even more effective.

It is estimated that the world demand for mercury could exceed the known world supply in about twenty years.[7] Yet the paper industry, among others, allows mercury to bleed into rivers and lakes until there is now about 163 million pounds free in the environment. Today's DDT will remain toxic only until about 2000, but mercury has a toxic life of at least a hundred years. Technology for recycling mercury is known, equipment is available, and the recycled metal brings about $7 a ton. Mercury-using industries should be *compelled* to recycle before any more mercury is transferred from the pulp mill to the food chain. If we run out of mercury by 1990 because the known world supply has been washed into the sea, all fish will be poisonous to a starving world.

In spite of the holdbacks, the trend is definitely toward a recycled economy. Being the world's major consumer is making recycling inevitable. The fact that we're also the world's major importer and polluter should hasten the inevitable. How much longer can the environment give up 25 tons of raw materials to support each of us every year?

The other nations are trying as hard as they can to approach our "appetite for metals" as well as other resources. If we could move as close to a totally recycled economy as is possible, not only would our lifestyles begin to make ecological sense, but our example might encourage other nations.

7. Thomas P. Lovering, *Resources and Man*, p. 128.

Discovering the Lost Trash Mine

The Bureau of Mines estimated a few years ago that 3 million tons of iron and 200,000 tons of other metals are lost in municipal incinerators each year, and that residues from many incinerators are richer than commercial ores of copper, zinc, aluminum, and other metals.[8] Former Director of Mines Walter R. Hibbard, writing in *Science* magazine a few years ago, termed it criminal negligence to continue making cars and major appliances less durable than they could be and not designing them so they can more easily be recycled.

The loss of metal to areas other than incineration must be incalculable. Were we a recycled, rather than waste-producing, society, we would allow raw ore only to replace metal unavoidably lost by wear or attrition and a smaller amount to meet controlled new demand: the trash mines could supply by far the bulk of an ongoing stabilized consumption.

The major problem in recycling is separating each material from the manufactured mix of paper, wood, glass, plastic, metal, and rubber, particularly with automobiles. The plastic in cars must be removed, usually by hand, before the carcass can be melted; if cars were designed for recycling, plastic components such as dashboards would unplug easily and other plastic use would be minimized.

8. *Man, An Endangered Species*, U.S. Department of the Interior Yearbook, Number 4, 1967, p. 79.

As it is, plastic used in carmaking is expected to more than triple to 2 billion pounds a year by 1980. Japan is ahead of us, having a series of furnaces to cook metals out of old cars at selective temperatures. If we copied the Japanese, the 8 million cars we junk yearly could become a national asset. We're testing grinders that reduce car hulks to small chunks for reuse as well as mixing molten iron with tin-plated steel cans and other types of scrap metal in correct proportions for steelmaking. So far, however, this recycling is only experimental.

Reynolds Aluminum first began offering bounties on aluminum cans in 1967 in Miami—a half cent each. Reynolds has since opened other collection centers and other manufacturers are beginning to do likewise. More than a million cans are recycled each year, a small dent in the annual avalanche of 5 billion cans.*

We are also beginning to think about recycling tires. Goodyear Tire and Rubber Company is experimenting with processes to cook out oils and tars and produce carbon black to reuse as a strengthener in new tires. If this process is profitable, up to one-third of our annual production of 100 million tires could be recycled. Other experiments include the extraction of chemicals from tires to be used in other manufacturing; someday, these

---

* For recycling information and an up-to-date list of aluminum redemption centers where used aluminum can be brought or shipped for resale (about 10 cents a pound), contact: Reynolds Metal Company, Metal Recycling Division, P.O. Box 27003, Richmond, Virginia 23261; Adolph Coors Company, Golden Gate, Colorado 80401; "Can-do," Kaiser Aluminum and Chemical Corporation, Room 870, Kaiser Center, 300 Lakeside Drive, Oakland, California 94604; Aluminum Company of America, 1501 Alcoa Building, Pittsburgh, Pennsylvania 15219.

processes might consume the remaining two-thirds of the tire production.

Combustion wastes are being looked at as sources of various chemicals and minerals. American Cyanamid is experimenting with benzothiazole removed from smoke-stack gasses for reuse in dyemaking. Unburned stack residue, fly ash, is being tried as an additive in pavement, fertilizer, and tire rubber, and as a water depollutant. Sulphur dioxide is a rich resource; methods are being tested for removing it from stack gases and making sulphuric acid for industrial processes.

Industrial waste water is likewise beginning to be prospected and is yielding ferrous sulphide from waste acids in wire manufacture; hydrogen sulphide and ammonia from oil refining; sugar and protein from desalted whey, which is otherwise a 20 billion gallons a year water-polluting waste from dairy products; and "tall oil," a vegetable oil waste from paperboard and packaging, of potential value in foods and cosmetics, which formerly washed into our rivers and lakes as a stinking and troublesome scum from brown-paper manufacture.

Most of these reclamation efforts are pollution-abatement schemes rather than attempts at recycling, just as the recycling experiments are often motivated in attempts to forestall legislation, especially in the aluminum-can situation. These attempts deserve and require our cooperation; if they become profitable, other makers of disposables will jump in. It is, after all, far better to get a good public image as well as a modest profit from recycling your product than to have the product banned entirely at the federal level or, as is already happening, banned in a troublesome national patchwork of local ordinances.

Certain manufacturers—Goodyear Tire and Rubber is one—suggest rather strongly that the expense of recycling experiments should be borne by the public through tax money in the form of "incentives." Other manufacturers feel that recycling expenses, like pollution-abatement costs, should be paid by the consumer in the form of higher prices. However, another argument is based on the premise that profit is a privilege of being allowed to do business in the public marketplace. Surely an obligation of this should be that business will be done in a way to not needlessly deplete resources or poison the environment, which are not "private" property at all. In this view, if the cost of manufacturing a given product is raised because of recycling or antipollution methods, this is a legitimate cost and should be paid out of profits.

Notice how rarely this line of reasoning is raised by either manufacturers or politicians when "the environment" is being moaned over. If you follow their statements closely, you will notice that the sanctity of profit margin is never questioned. Perhaps if ecological citizens raised a voice, recycling and clean-up programs would become an integral part of profiting from our common resources and ecosystems.

Industrial recycling should be instituted with as much urgency as possible in view of coming depletions. Even full recycling will not make for a perpetual industrial society, but the attrition of Earth's resources will at least be slowed. If recycling comes to industry only as dire necessity forces it, civilization will be too close to depletion's brink for it to last long.

Thomas S. Lovering has said: "When the time comes for living in a society dependent on scrap for high grade metal and on common rocks for commercial ore, the affluent society will be much overworked to maintain a standard of living equal to that of a century ago." [9]

Our Packaged Society

If modern society is what it packages, we're the most meticulously articulated people of all time—from the deluge of ideas, emotions, and procedures packaged in film, tape, and paper to the almost 100 percent packaging of all material products.

The concept of packaging edibles for transportation and storage comes from Napoleon, who commissioned the development of food containers as a tactical advantage for his far-ranging army. The invention proved such a success in military logistics that containerized food and drink rapidly became basic to civilian lifestyle. Packaging became an extension of man's range, sophisticated in our time to the space capsule, human life packaged for storage and transportation to the moon.

At $29 billion a year, packaging is the fourth largest industry in the country and is basic to our civilization, but its glut of nondisposable "disposables" has created a crisis unique in history.

On a per capita basis, we each toss out over a pound and a half of packaging each day; this costs us each about $50 a year. Those fancy, bright packages are by no means free or a "bonus." Some cost nearly as much as their contents are worth: beer, for instance, costs 43 percent for the can; baby food costs 36 percent for the

9. *Resources and Man*, p. 130.

jar; a quart of motor oil would cost 26 percent less without the can. One-fifth of your total spending is to buy the wastepaper, crushed plastic, broken glass, and dirty metal cans choking incinerators and dumps around the country.

On a per capita basis, we each toss out 135 glass jars and bottles a year; add metal cans, and we each dispose of one strong container every day. Add paper and plastic and the volume more than doubles. Per capita figures are misleading; obviously individual consumption varies tremendously—far fewer empty jelly jars come from the Northern Cheyenne Reservation in Montana than from Great Neck, Long Island. An increasing proportion of these containers in our personal 7 pounds of trash each day are immune to natural decay and will remain scattered over the earth longer than the oldest cave paintings have lasted. Divers report that the deepest floors of the Atlantic are littered with bottles and cans.

More than 50 million tons of raw materials go into packaging each year, and this figure is shooting up well ahead of population increase. Glass is a packaging staple and, although by no means the material of greatest increase (plastic volume and aluminum percentage claim the honor), glass consumption in packaging indicates the general trend in over-all package consumption.

The following figures are adapted from *Resources in America's Future* for shipments of glass containers at various dates:[10]

	billion containers
1929—	4.9
1932—	3.9
1944—	12.7

10. Landsberg, et al., *Resources.*

1970—	31.7*
1980—	44.8
	57.6 (H)
2000—	82.1
	136.8 (H)

The Great Depression and wartime recovery stand out in this table; from 1932 to the present, glass containers grew by 800 percent and by the end of the century are expected to increase at least 260 percent. Thirty years from now, in 2000, each American can throw 20 bottles out his car windows for each one tossed out today.

Projections for other packaging materials show similar or greater increases.

million tons

Steel:	1948—	5.5
	1970—	8.3
	2000—	10.6
		23.2 (H)

We can hardly expect the rest of humanity to rejoice at our plans to waste up to 300 percent more of this resource in thirty years.

million tons

Aluminum:	1952—	0.03
	1970—	0.43
	2000—	1.22
		2.28 (H)

Again, while our population will not double, use of aluminum could increase 500 percent in the projected period, nearly all of it imported.

* This, remember, is the medium projection, the actual figure for 1970 exceeded 36 billion.

	million tons
Paper: 1946—	10.42
1970—	25.53
2000—	75.8
	114.0 (H)

Even as the timber resources shrink before our eyes, we plan to waste three or four times as much paper in 2000 as today.

Consider all the trash around you today, in the streets, by the highways, in the parks, on the sidewalk, flowing out of well-packed dumps, blackening the sky from incineration. Visualize the projections coming true: three steel cans and five aluminum ones for every one you see today; four times the broken glass everywhere; three milk cartons flattened in the gutter for each one today. Unburnable paper has been invented—*imagine* the disaster it portends. The figures used above from *Resources* are for total national use, and include a moderate population increase, but the real problem is not so much the increase of users as the rise in solid waste from increased packaging per capita. Even as early as 1976, individual package use will rise substantially, as indicated by figures adapted from the Department of Health, Education and Welfare:

pounds per capita *used in*	1958	1970	1976 *(projection)*
paper	189	284	332
metal	72	73	76
glass	68	92	107
plastic	4	18	28
other	71	111	118
total	404	578	661

These figures are for *each* of us and indicate that we will use, and dispose of, fully 257 pounds *more* packaging in 1976 than we did in 1958, and 83 pounds more than we each are throwing away this year.

Glass comprises about 6 percent of today's solid waste, and gestures toward recycling a tiny part of today's tens of billions of glass containers are under way, but the most obvious step—banning nonreturnable bottles— has yet to take place. The next step would be to either ban or put a deposit on aluminum cans; their value per can is only half a penny, so the deposit would have to be increased to at least 10 cents to help motivate return. In view of how rapidly deposit bottles disappear, the "profit" from aluminum cans not returned would go to the appropriate government level to defray costs of picking up the cans—most states spend 25 to 30 cents to retrieve *each* can from the highway (just pickup, not disposal).

The third step in reducing container consumption calls for standardized glass packaging with deposit. Would life be unbearably dreary if all 8-ounce mustard jars were identical from brand to brand and identical to jars used for mayonnaise, jams, and jellies? All fruit juices could come in identical reusable jars which, when returned, could be refilled with vegetable juice or pickles or whatever else comes in jars of equivalent volume. It's the confusion of sizes and shapes which makes bottles and jars prohibitively expensive to reuse. One estimate puts the total number of containers to be produced in five years at 100 billion—we certainly don't need 500 containers each for our yearly consumption. The three steps outlined above could cut this total to 5 or 6 billion or less.

Because the savings would be in favor of the consumer at the expense of the expanding packaging industry, we could expect strong industrial resistance. Certain supermarket chains would have to be persuaded too. First

National Stores, for example, has 444 outlets on the East Coast which refuse to sell deposit containers. But the move toward returnables is indicated by pending legislation in twenty-five states to ban nonreturnable bottles. Finland has already banned them; Denmark is about to; the Canadian province of British Columbia will require deposits on all beverage bottles *and cans* starting in 1971. Bills are before Congress to ban one-way bottles and even all nonreturnable beverage containers.

To anticipate pending legislation, container manufacturers are opening "redemption centers" where their glass and metal products can be returned. Glass, for instance, is bought back for a penny a pound at about a hundred centers, with more opening every year. The glass is crushed for making new glass or for other uses: "glasphalt" is a paving material; the glass may also be used for building blocks and glass-wool insulation, or as a sand substitute in concrete. Glass containers are increasing at 5 percent a year; the redemption program at best wouldn't even absorb the annual increase and at present is able to absorb less than 3 percent of the more than 36 billion jars and bottles produced in 1970. At most, glass makers hope to eventually be able to recycle 30 percent of their production, but this will require full public cooperation.

The redemption center program is not an alternative to the steps previously suggested; rather, it is the fourth step in trying to control our consumption of raw materials. There is doubtless a redemption center near where you live; for a complete and up-to-date list, write:

Glass Container Manufacturer's Institute
330 Madison Avenue
New York City

The Song of the Plastic Bottle

The impact of plastic on today's society can hardly be measured; its impact on tomorrow's world can scarcely be imagined. In 1960, Americans used less than 10 billion pounds of plastic. In the year 2000, we are projected to use betwen 73 and 215 billion pounds: few trends are projected to increase between 700 and 2100 percent. Plastic used as a manmade skin, as in coats, is a great relief to nature, sparing the skins of animals, and represents a triumph of our technological evolution. The plastic used in packaging, a convenience for mankind, is hardly a relief for our environment.

Plastic comes primarily from either the forest or the oil field. Cellophane is still used to make half the total of transparent films. This wood-based material was introduced in 1924 and the considerable technology developed for its high speed printing and wrapping has only recently been challenged by newer techniques for handling petroleum-based films such as vinyl, polyethylene, and polyvinyl chloride or the related polyvinyidene chloride used in such products as Saran Wrap. The shift now is away from cellophane, and by 2000, petrochemical films are expected to comprise 90 percent of the market. There will still be two to ten times as much cellophane as today, but between five and eighteen times more petrochemical films. As the number of consumers isn't expected to increase by more than 70 percent, each consumer is apparently expected to use ten times more plastic wrap than now. Whether or not this comes true is up to us.

Twenty years ago, we each used under 2.5 pounds of plastic in a year's packaging; today it is over 10 pounds, and by 2000 it's projected to be between 23 and 80 pounds a year. The difficulty of getting rid of the million tons of plastic from our packages could be fourteen times worse by then. *Resources in America's Future* provides the following figures for the rise of plastic in packaging:[11]

billion pounds

1950—0.36	
1970—2.03	
1980—3.82	
2000—8.04	
28.31 (H)	

Plastic bottles and containers are petrochemical varieties, one of the newest being polyvinyl chloride, or PVC. In 1960, we each used about a pound's worth of plastic bottles; today we use over 3 pounds each, but by 2000 we're projected to each use between 9 and 43 pounds. These per capita figures combine to make a staggering total volume—as a nation we'll go from our present 680 million pounds of plastic bottles to between 3.2 and 15 billion pounds at the century's end. Meanwhile, we consume (or really only empty) over 3 billion plastic bottles a year, or 15 per capita. By 2000 we could be throwing out, per capita, over 200 plastic bottles annually. What this per capita figure means in terms of real consumers is unknown, but the chorus of plastic bottles will be deafening, for this is the area of greatest package growth.

If we could give away our plastic bottles, it would be

11. Landsberg, et al., *Resources*, p. 701.

only one year before every human on earth had his own plastic bottle. Each year's production includes 200 million PVC bottles, eternally enduring containers. PVC is also used as "shrink wrapping" for everything from meat to books—100 million pounds of PVC are produced every year as transparent film. The FDA has approved PVC as a food and drink container, so the era of the PVC pop bottle is not far away. We are expected to be consuming 4 billion plastic bottles by 1973, and PVC might comprise the greatest growth in this production.

PVC is a good example of why a material should not be allowed into mass production simply because it is technically and economically possible. PVC will never degrade naturally—long after our sun goes out, space archaeologists will discover strata upon strata of PVC bottles, all like new. Should our sun go supernova, or explode before dying, and engulf the earth in flames, each PVC bottle and piece of PVC wrap will give off 60 percent of its weight as hydrogen chloride gas. This is the problem of PVC—it cannot be burned without releasing corrosive and poisonous hydrogen chloride. The toxic gas kills vegetation and endangers humans around incinerators where PVC is burned; the incinerators themselves become gummed, corroded, and must be shut down for repair. Even a few PVC bottles can contaminate the total load being burned, and there is no way for PVC to be separated, or even detected, at the incinerator—or on the supermarket shelf. PVC is generally soft and transparent, but because other, less damaging, plastics are similar to PVC, the best we can do is shun any kind of soft, transparent bottle or wrap until PVC is off the market.

But *all* forms of plastic packaging present disposal problems. It becomes waste almost immediately, and although the 20 billion pounds of plastic produced this year comprise only a minor part of the year's 700 billion pounds of solid waste, the plastic doesn't go away unless burned: once a plastic bottle, always a plastic bottle. At present there is no type of plastic which can be recycled or biodegraded, and not all types can safely be burned. Waste plastic cannot be made into new plastic; in fact, one of the difficulties of plastic manufacture is how to dispose of the scraps.

Add to the four steps given earlier for controlling disposable containers this fifth: required federal licensing of every new material, especially plastic, intended for packages involved in interstate commerce. The plastic manufacturer would have to prove that his product could in fact be disposed of, if not recycled, at mass production volumes before a package license would be given. Such a regulation would keep PVC film and bottles off the market, though this material could still be used for other purposes. PVC is bonded to either side of glass (polymer-coated glass), and the qualities which make the plastic so unfortunate for packaging combine to make a superior safety glass. PVC can also be used in furniture making. We must come to terms with the special problems of plastic disposal before the deluge truly begins. The list of plastics being developed and introduced is growing so rapidly that the Food and Drug Administration cannot test them all, and tests only those to be used for food and drink packaging. But testing should be industry's responsibility. If you agree, suggest it to your Senators and to your Congressman.

There are three basic ways plastic can be improved as a disposable package: make it burnable, make it biodegradable, make it recyclable. If a plastic bottle can be safely and easily burned, it is at least disposable, although this is still a waste of resources. Barex 210 is a plastic resin developed by Vistron Corporation, part of Standard Oil of Ohio (Sohio), which "can be easily and safely burned without emitting annoying or noxious gases," according to Dr. James D. Idol, of Sohio.[12] The FDA has approved Barex, which burns as readily as cardboard, and the plastic was recently test-marketed in Las Vegas as a drink container by Pepsi Cola. If all factors are positive in other tests, Barex may at least save us from the PVC pop bottle.

Biodegradable plastic would have an advantage over burnable plastic in that by nourishing the microbes involved in decomposition it could be a soil builder. Word emerges periodically from research laboratories of a plastic which, when broken, will slowly revert to a puddle of quickly disappearing liquid. British researchers have patented a plastic formula containing special dyes which, when exposed to sunlight's ultraviolet rays, cause the plastic to disintegrate to a powder digestible by soil bacteria. Glass filters ultraviolet rays from sunlight, so bottles inside would be safe. The normally colorless dyes become increasingly tinted as they begin to work, giving sufficient warning so a bleach bottle, for instance, wouldn't suddenly crumble in your hand. The action of the dyes can be timed to disintegrate the container from two weeks to three months after exposure to sunlight. How well this system would work on bottles buried under other trash and thus shielded from sunlight is not known, but hopefully the American plastics industry is following British research.

The best answer is reused or recycled bottles. Plastic

12. Reported in *Investor's Reader*, Merrill Lynch, Pierce, Fenner, and Smith, Inc., December 2, 1970.

food containers probably cannot be sterilized for reuse because the heat would deform them, but detergent and bleach bottles could presumably be washed and reused. Direct reuse is, however, doubtlessly more expensive than simply making new containers, even if redemption centers were operated at community expense. Most plastic packaging is thermoplastic, which can be heated and formed into new shapes; the many kinds of plastic now used, however, present an overwhelming problem of separation. If the plastic industry standardized use of one or two types of recyclable plastic, these containers could be collected and shredded for melting; such an innovation hardly seems beyond such a sophisticated industry. To some extent, a recyclable plastic might reduce the profits of an industry which otherwise enjoys a massive one-way production, but it is the best of all possible solutions. The manufacturers of other containers—notably glass and aluminum—have begun to recognize their social responsibility, and it is time plastic makers follow suit. Burning and decomposing will get rid of the plastic, but why waste the petroleum resource if it can be recycled? Urge your support for development of a standardized, recyclable plastic packaging material to:

Society of the Plastics Industry
250 Park Avenue
New York City 10017

It isn't always possible to avoid plastic containers, but we should do so whenever possible. Whenever you do avoid a specific brand because of its plastic package, be sure to write the maker of the product *as well as* the Society of the Plastics Industry. A consumer votes by purchase and registers that vote by writing at least one letter. Your letter will be magnified several hundred-fold, as manufacturers assume there are many others who feel the same but who don't bother to write. If a carton of shredded plastic containers accompanies your letter to the Society, perhaps they'll understand the song of the plastic bottle better.

Newspaper—Save the Paper, Change the News

The future is closing in on our forests. Paper and other wood-pulp products aren't really cheap, they only seem to be because we're able to cut, for a year's supply, from all the millions of trees which have grown during our lifetime. When this legacy is logged out the price of all timber products, including paper, will *soar*. Expanded production of any wood use, housing, furniture, fine paper, will have to be balanced to equal timber growth when the remaining supply of forest is consumed in less than twenty years.

"Interest" from our forest reserves should be spent only for essentials, such as housing, synthetics, and furniture; instead, we are burning through the reserves themselves, turning them to paper and only recycling 20 percent of this huge wasteful production. During World War II, we recycled 60 percent of our paper; during the dark resource depression which will accompany depletions indicated in a previous chapter, total paper recycling will be a sober business if there is to be any maintenance of literacy, let alone expansion of it here or in the Third World.

Paper and other wood-pulp products account for about half of our solid waste; newsprint alone comprises 14 percent. Waste cellulose fiber is a major disposal problem for makers of cardboard boxes, disposable diapers, milk cartons, and others. Paper used in packaging will soar, as noted earlier, between seven and eleven times above today's level—or will if enough forest exists to be consumed. Even as International Paper Company advertises the "disposable environment," however, the depressing shrink of our forest resources is reflected in the emergence of new uses for waste wood pulp and an increasing pressure to recycle newsprint.

This very moderate trend toward slowly increased recycling is more than countered by the growth of timber exports and the constant advertising to increase paper consumption. We will need 7 billion more board feet of timber by 1978; although the softwood export to Japan alone exceeds 2 billion board feet annually now, the National Forest Products Association (the timber industry's lobby) is pushing to increase the allowable cut in the National Forests. Even if member corporations of the NFPA were not clutching long-term timber commitments to Japan, our National Forests shouldn't be further eliminated when we could be doing at least three times better with recycling.

C. R. Gutermuth, vice president of the Wildlife Management Institute, put it succinctly: "They [the timber industry] have been cutting the hell out of their own lands [to maintain exports to Japan] and depending on the Government to bail them out by permitting excessive cutting in the national forests." [13]

We're already over 5 million board feet behind in re-

13. Reported in the *New York Times*, June 16, 1970. (Brackets are the *Times'*.)

foresting areas previously logged in the National Forests, and money for closing this gap—let alone reforesting each year's increase—is not forthcoming. We cannot allow further National Forest sacrifice. We should get completely out of the National Forests until they can regrow. At that time, we should cut only less than is growing and that only after recycling is in effect. Our forests are holding together some of the most important ecosystems and cycles on the planet; keeping them intact from ravages of greed, fire, and pollution is one of the important contributions this generation can make to the next.

Wastepaper alone amounts to 58.5 million tons a year in America, of which over 8 million tons are newsprint. Formerly, paper in general and newspaper in particular could be recycled only for lower end-uses, not the same use, because the ink couldn't be removed. Garden State Paper Company, of Garfield, New Jersey, which makes 5 percent of America's newsprint, pioneered a deinking process and is now recycling over 340,000 tons of old newsprint into new newsprint a year: the printing changes, but the paper stays. There's no reason the rest of the 8 million tons a year cannot be recycled. If this were done, upwards of 8 billion gallons of water would not have to be polluted by pulp mills. More important, 150 million fewer trees could be cut without reducing newsprint consumption. Each year until 2000 that saved forest could grow; each year it would increase by 150 million trees. This one area of recycling alone would enable us to create, at no lowering of consumption, a growing Forest Trust for future generations.

The National Academy of Sciences recently suggested that we will be recycling 35 percent of our paper by 1985, when total paper consumption will be about twice today's level. In view of timber shortages, we should set this goal a full decade earlier—35 percent by 1975 at the *latest*. Unfortunately, the main difficulty is in transportation of the waste from collection to factory; transportation accounts for about 90 percent of the expense of all recycling, including paper. In this area, International Paper Company, whose "disposable environment" was criticized earlier, is to be commended; International has for several years been a net purchaser of waste—i.e., they have been recycling paper. So far, most of our recycled paper has come, in order, from corrugated boxes, paper from office buildings, and newspapers. Of all corrugated boxes made in 1969, 25 percent were recycled, compared with only 23 percent of the year's newspapers.

The Louisville *Times* and *Courier-Journal* in Kentucky will begin recycling part of their daily circulation of 95 tons of newsprint, using the Garden State Paper de-inking techniques. The move is aimed at relieving the solid-waste burden on municipal incineration by 30 percent, but, if all 95 tons are eventually recycled, it will also save over 1,600 trees a day.

Recycling should be urged upon major newspapers such as the *New York Times* and the Los Angeles *Times*. Each *New York Times* Sunday edition is about 6 pounds, of which only an estimated average of 1.5 pounds are actually read. The rest of the "fat" could easily be avoided if the huge edition were sold section-by-section, so readers could buy only those sections they wanted to read. But the *New York Times* opposes sectioned sale on the grounds that this would destroy the "entity" of "total coverage." Actually it also means they can't make huge circulation promises to all advertisers in all sections. The *New York Times* also opposes a suggested disposal tax, which would raise the price of the Sunday edition 6 cents. As long as the *Times* opposes both suggestions, the least she could do is recycle herself.

Garden State Paper, which recycles newsprint for $7 a ton cheaper than virgin newsprint can be produced, was tried by the *Times* for a short while; the recycled newsprint was found to be as good as virgin newsprint, but the *Times* refuses to use it regularly because of existing contracts with suppliers in Maine and Canada. Should the *Times* become a good ecological citizen and totally recycle, its huge new business would make recycled newsprint even cheaper, far more competitive with virgin newsprint, and encourage other newspapers to save money by recycling too. If it weren't for the *Times* policy, 6,150,000 trees a year could be spared. And the City of New York would be able to allot some of the $10 million now spent disposing of the year's old *Times* to more pressing social and environmental needs which the *Times* so often endorses. *Times* editorials are eloquent on behalf of forests and conservation while the paper itself maintains a policy against a very simple, proven method of making a substantial contribution to forest conservation.

The Los Angeles *Times* is the largest newsprint consumer in the West and, although Garden State Paper has a branch in nearby Pomona, the Los Angeles *Times* prefers to get virgin newsprint from its own sources in Oregon and Canada.

Newspapers all around the country could now be using recycled newsprint, using virgin newsprint only to meet increases in circulation or to replace whatever is lost in recycling. If this were done by 1980, it could result in saving 190 million trees a year; by 2000, the forest saving would be between 272 and 357 million trees annually.

One ton of virgin pulp requires about 3.6 acres of forest; if the paper-consuming industries recycled half their paper, this alone would spare 500 million trees a year and would free a forest area equal to all the New England states, plus Maryland, Pennsylvania, New York, and New Jersey.

Newspapers are the most obvious, but not the only major source of paper waste. Consider the millions of telephone books the Bell System replaces periodically. In Manhattan the White Pages and the Yellow Pages are separate books, each weighing over 5 pounds. Whenever we get new ones garbage cans are clogged with the old ones; old phone books should certainly be collected for recycling when the new ones are distributed.

If we recycled all wastepaper, we could leave over a billion trees standing every year which otherwise end up in the incinerator or blowing along the highway. We spare 200 million trees a year with current recycling, and for every additional ton of paper we could reuse, we would avoid cutting 17 more trees.[14]

If you are an average paper consumer, your lifestyle requires that 11 trees be cut each year to provide your waste. If you could personally cut consumption, share consumption by sharing newspapers and magazines, and have what you do consume recycled, there would be, scattered over the continent, a grove of trees increasing each year in proportion to your eco-mindedness.

The survival of our species depends on the health of many other species of animals and plants seemingly remote from urban readers of the *New York Times,* yet each additional tree we don't consume contributes to the aggregate holding action against the planned destruction of the forest. This could be our most meaningful per-

14. National Association of Secondary Material Industries, Inc., *Recycling Resources,* 1970.

sonal contribution to the preservation of the environment. Describe your support for paper recycling to:

Association of Pulp Consumers
American Paper and Pulp Association
American Paper Institute, Inc.
260 Madison Avenue
New York City

The above groups share a skyscraper, but must be separately addressed.

American Newspaper Publisher's Association
730 Third Avenue
New York City

American Pulpwood Association
605 Third Avenue
New York City

If you feel the National Forests should be allowed to regrow, or at least be sustained and not cut for exportation, contact the timber industry's lobby, which they've cleverly named after their prey:

National Forest Products Association
1619 Massachusetts Avenue
Washington, D.C.

Trash Is Cash

Environmental Action Coalition
235 East 49th Street
New York City 10017

Keep your thumb on this address; you'll probably want to contact them regarding their Trash Is Cash program. The Coalition, which sponsored New York City's Earth Day, has begun a program to reduce the city's solid-waste load by 30 percent. Trash Is Cash is helping neighborhoods open recycling centers, such as one manned by children at 315 East 61st Street; profits, although small, are being realized, and in the example cited are being used to improve the neighborhood by paying for trees and park equipment. Other recycling programs operated by church or school groups can provide funds for scholarships or local environmental projects. The Girl Scouts recycle garbage as well as sell cookies nowadays. At some centers, for instance, housewives bring in a month's worth of newspapers and aluminum cans, and leave with a handful of trading stamps.

Residents of New York City can get the phone numbers of local redemption centers from the Coalition. If you live elsewhere, why not start one (the Coalition can provide advice on how to do it). To quote a Coalition mailing: "Group involvement must be actively sought. One person will not make a very large dent in the community solid waste program, but 20 or 30 active people could tremendously reduce the solid waste or any other problem."

Although prices for recycled materials will vary with your location and the availability of local industry which can use recycled materials, the following are approximate prices:

Aluminum	....	$200 a ton
Tin	....	30 a ton
Rags	....	20 a ton
Glass	....	20 a ton
Newsprint	....	8 a ton
Bimetal cans	....	5 a ton

Collection sites should be set up in convenient locations—churches, supermarkets, shopping centers, schools. Keep the site clean, don't let it have the air of a garbage dump. More important, however, is finding a market for the trash after it has been collected and separated.

Beginning March 20, 1971, selected Coca-Cola bottling plants began doubling as recycling depots, buying any brand's glass bottle or aluminum can for one-half cent apiece (except Coca-Cola bottles, which bring 5 cents). The glass must be separated by color, but Coca Cola will crush and resell it, at no profit, to be reused; the aluminum cans will be melted by Reynolds Metals Company and will be reused. Call the Coca-Cola bottling plant in your area to see if they are participating. If they aren't, ask that they do (or ask another bottling plant). By all means participate in this program if you can; so much of private enterprise's ecological awareness is negative that if public indifference causes the few excellent attempts, such as Coca-Cola's, to fail, even the most callous of corporations will have a good rationalization for doing nothing about their eco-corruption.

If you live among the 80 percent of urbanized Americans, there is doubtlessly a variety of markets. *Trash Into Cash*, by Jerry Mack, lists 500 names and addresses of places to sell collected trash.* Also, contact any local breweries or bottling companies, supermarket chains, secondhand, salvage, or surplus stores. Check out the Yellow Pages under Junk, Scrap, or more specific headings such as Rags, Bottles, Metals. If there is a college in your area, it no doubt has an ecology action group; contact them, any Boy Scout or Girl Scout troup, or a high school service club to help staff the collection center or assist in separating trash. Service and civic groups

* Available from: Textbooks, P.O. Box 3862, San Angelo, Texas 76901.

can help by providing a collection site; (behind the Elk's Lodge, for example). Members of the Chamber of Commerce could provide the most valuable service by persuading local industries to pick up and use the trash from collection centers. Ladies' clubs are persuasive and often effective.

The trash must be separated before it can be sold; separate aluminum, tin-lined cans (most food cans with side seams), steel cans (most beverage cans with side seams), bimetal cans (beverage cans with seams and pull-tab aluminum tops). Separate glass according to color: clear, green, brown, amber. Dirty containers should be rinsed unless the buying industry includes washing as part of its process. Labels should be stripped and cans flattened. Bimetal cans should have their aluminum tops removed; the bimetal can must go two ways. For this reason alone, we should avoid them in favor of cans which are of a single metal type, preferably steel (if it is not recycled, at least it will rust).

Paper also must be separated: newspapers from magazines from cardboard from "other." Bale the newspapers with twine, not wire. Each 36-inch stack is equal to one tree. Seventeen yard-high stacks will also save 60 thousand gallons of water from the pollution of 275 pounds of sulphur and 350 pounds of lime, as well as enough electricity to power a 100-watt bulb for the entire winter.

If consumers do the cleaning and separating, so much the better. If there is a collection site in your area, you should establish recycling habits so containers and paper are routinely prepared, separated, stored, and transported. If you have a garage or even just enough room for several large cardboard boxes for storage, a couple of children whom you can pay to clean and sort cans and jars, and a station wagon among your friends, the routine of not wasting your solid waste will be far easier. Join with a couple of neighbors for a common storage and return operation; even the smallest profit can be used for a commonly shared compost and garden maintenance, or other ecologically oriented projects.

"The Can People" (American Can Company, Continental Can Company, National Can Corporation) opened three Manhattan collection centers in February, 1971. In a full-page newspaper ad, they called for the return of any can that had been rinsed out and had its label removed. Any profits are promised for charity or worthy local projects. Hopefully "The Can People" will open similar centers in other areas. For information, write:

> American Can Company
> 100 Park Avenue
> New York City

One way or another, you should be able to get rid of a sizable amount of daily refuse. Even if there is no profit to you, there is a great saving of environment, though a fair amount of money can be made, especially by groups. Aluminum (cans, foil, chairs, anything) is worth the most; PVC is worth less than nothing; aerosol cans *under no circumstances* should be collected or stored (they present hazards to anyone, especially children, sorting and flattening). Preparing the trash for recycling for several families can be a good ongoing activity for kids, like mowing lawns or shoveling snow. A really enterprising operator gets the neighbors to pay a small amount for picking up their bulky container and paper trash, then sells it to the collection site. If you have a compacter, use it to crush glass and flatten cans (don't mix). If you don't have one, don't buy one: recycle and compost instead.

If you would like to encourage the experiments being done in large-scale recycling, send a good word to:

> American Iron and Steel Institute
> 150 East 42nd Street
> New York City 10017

Recycling Resources is a booklet, free upon request, which tells in illustrated detail the need for, present state of, and hoped-for improvement in recycling our national resources of metal, paper, and textiles. Over 25,000 copies have been sent out since Earth Day, 1970. Write for yours:

> National Association of Secondary Materials Industries, Inc.
> 300 Madison Avenue
> New York City 10017

In a depleting world, all "junk" should become "secondary materials."

On to the Recycled Society

It is generally estimated that of the 7 pounds of material we each waste every day, about 5.5 pounds eventually reach some kind of dump. Traditionally, the mix of garbage and trash is simply heaped in a secluded area just out of town; in some dumps, the pile is partially burned and covered with dirt. There are about 200,000 municipal dumps in our country, around three-quarters of them uncomplicated common heaps. Today half of them are overflowing, verminous, or otherwise officially termed "unsatisfactory." Of all the material, 73 percent simply lies there, 15 percent is burned, 8 percent is buried, but only 3 percent is salvaged and one percent is composted. This is the destination of half the natural resources consumed by the human race.

The pound and a half that doesn't reach the dump is litter. Nearly all of this is packaging—alone more than the total waste of the average human. Riverside dumps also contribute to litter. Rivers carry about 2 million gallons of sewage and 4 million pounds of animal excrement into the ocean every second; however, total river-borne litter has not yet been computed.

Upwards of 350 million tons of garbage is generated each year and 73 percent of it is dumped and forgotten; this unburned, unburied, and nonrecycled pile grows by over 230 million tons annually. Known as the "solid-waste crisis," this is half paper, about 15 percent packaging, 12 percent organic refuse such as food scraps and dead pets, 3 percent cloth; the remainder a mélange of contraceptive and sanitary items, burned-out light bulbs, dead batteries, failed toasters, and other technological sewage from the machine world.

One recent suggestion was to put garbage into the deepest trenches of the ocean; the marine trenches are moving slowly toward the center of the earth as they are squeezed by the weight of land masses. As marine trenches are the only parts of the planet going inward, anything dumped into them would not reappear for geologic ages. The trenches are sinking so slowly, however, that the garbage wouldn't be ground inward as rapidly as it was dumped; and although it's difficult to imagine actually filling the trenches, it's also hard to imagine them as geologic garbage disposal units, if only because of shipping costs.

New York City produces over 22,000 tons of garbage a day; the figure grows by 4 percent annually, and the city's landfill sites will be exhausted before 1980. There is presently a debate as to whether the city should invest a billion dollars each on four giant incinerators; critics say that the cost in extra air pollution the huge furnaces will create is too high, and that recycling alternates should be used. Even if much of the refuse cannot be recycled immediately, new techniques are emerging for shredding, baling, pulverizing, composting, high-temperature burning, and otherwise substantially reducing the volume of solid waste until facilities can be designed to recycle the colossal outpouring. Ecology, Inc., is opening a plant in Brooklyn which will turn 150 tons of garbage into lawn fertilizer every day. Composting could eventually reduce the burden of solid waste by half.

National Recycling Industries of New York City owns the largest fleet of industrial garbage trucks in the East and formerly paid more than half a million dollars a year in disposal fees to municipal dumps, but NRI is building recycling plants where the waste will eventually be sold back as Nutrifill, an organic fertilizer. The company is investing $15 million in a recycling plant for New York City which will turn 3,500 tons of solid waste a day into Nutrifill, purified drinking water, and electricity generated from 3000-degree burning of waste which cannot be composted. Such high-temperature burning consumes 97 percent of the waste, contributing very little to air pollution.

Because even farsighted companies such as Ecology, Inc., and National Recycling Industries must show a profit rather quickly from their recycling investments, these private firms are rare. Communities only spend more on highways and schools than they do for garbage disposal; with this kind of capital available, we could become a recycled society with only a little additional effort. The initial cost of starting nationwide recycling is high, but if a National Recycling Trust Fund were fed by small disposal taxes on nondurable manufactured items, similar to the Highway Trust Fund fed by automotive taxes, there would soon be billions of dollars available for loans to fund the establishment of community recycling centers. The proportion of nondurables in the GNP of the year 2000 is projected to grow 3 to 5 times greater than it is today. The total GNP is expected to increase several times over today's level, and the rise in its share of nondurables (which rapidly become solid waste) means that up to five times more within that huge GNP will be instant garbage.

If the rising proportion of nondurables in the rising total production is taxed for disposal, it would provide a growing tax base for the Recycling Fund. Added to funds now spent scattershot for sewage improvement or dump enlargement, the Recycling Fund could finance centralized community centers where sewage and solid waste would be combined—finally ending the tradition, dating back before ancient Egypt, of dumping sewage into rivers.

Municipal laws could be passed requiring everyone use at least three garbage cans (plastic, to cut noise), color-coded for separation of contents. Organic refuse such as kitchen wastes and lawn clippings would go into one, metal and plastic into another, and glass into a third. If a sanitation man found a can containing "illegal" contents, he would ticket it, and the fine would go into the Fund. If the cans could be made from recycled plastic, they might be provided free.

Garbage trucks would be redesigned on a modular basis; one module or bin for each type of waste. Four bins would be required, one for each can and another for baled newspapers and magazines.

At the recycling center, the trucks could be "turned around" more rapidly than they can now—the filled modules would be lifted out of place and empty ones dropped in. The trucks could go for a second collection almost without stopping. In large suburban areas, the modules could go to collection depots for reshipment to the center.

It may seem inconceivable that the sea of filth we produce could ever be adequately recycled, but either we find a way out, or resign ourselves to sinking beneath its surface. If even a tiny portion of our technological attention were spent designing the GNP for recycling, recycling centers would show tremendous profit. Scientists at the Bureau of Mines research center in Pittsburgh have produced a technique for converting a ton of garbage into a barrel of crude oil; converting only one percent of our solid waste into oil would provide nearly 6 million gallons of fuel each year.

At the recycling center, metal and plastic would be sorted by magnets, floatation, and selective melting; most glass would be automatically color sorted, the remainder ground up for uses previously mentioned. Sewage would be combined with the organic 60 percent of household garbage and rapidly composted in warm, aerated vats "seeded" with microbes. The by-product, methane gas, would fuel the trucks and generate power for the center; the compost would be free for rebuilding eroded or worn out crop or forest land. Nonreusable plastic could be shredded and heat-compressed into building blocks for other centers or for housing. Only after the national re-cycled output had been consigned could any new metal, oil, glass, plastic, forest products, or synthetic fertilizer be produced. If the draft still exists, recycling could be an alternate service.

Even without the fusion torch, the ultimate in recy-cling—the solar-scale temperatures would vaporize all garbage into 92 separate elements—recycling centers would be profitable. As it is, we are moving haphazardly with small isolated experiments in recycling, duplicat-ing waste-disposal facilities by not centralizing them, and supporting myriad failing proposals for "upgrading" what is essentially an inappropriate basic approach to waste disposal. Centralized recycling centers, located to service many small communities, would consolidate our efforts and bring the garbage into fewer but much greater heaps, which is necessary if recycling is to be optimally profitable. The garbage problem is presently so out of control that only such a Draconian approach can hope to remedy it.

Ghetto residents are often so demoralized by their environment that they throw garbage out the window into their trashy, bleak world, rather than bother to carry it down to the street. One more tin can or rat doesn't insult an environment crowded with rats and tin cans; as our dumps bloat and gag and the trash mounts around us, we are all moved behaviorally toward that same sink where tolerance for filth is increased and motivation for survival is decreased. Why bother taxing ourselves for recycling centers, why separate garbage, why push for standardized containers, why return bot-tles when gravity will easily remove them from our hand? The end of this train of thought is "what's posterity done for us?"

To suggest that we learn to act in concert in a planned, directed way is not to suggest that we all wear uniforms and eat only controlled portions of standardized food from dreary and identical containers, but there is a point where total freedom of consumption in an overcrowded world becomes moribund—and we have reached and passed that point.

Rudyard Kipling said that words are the most powerful drug used by mankind; our literate, articulated, well-argued concept of nature and of our own impending demise may actually be the terminal symptom. Ecology is good copy and a good scare, like the monster movie—after the pollution documentary on television, we change channels and are equally breathless at the emergence of the creature from 20,000 fathoms. If our sense of peril is truly so abstract, we're probably finished—look at the way industry and government play an abstract chess game with the pollution issue. The oil companies, which, aside from nuclear energy, monopolize the energy business in America, alternately woo and deceive us with advertising while proclaiming oil and gas shortages even as they increase exports to Japan and destroy life-supporting ecosystems in search of more fuel. We debate, we argue—when we finally become ready to "do something," the problem will have become insuperable.

We are going to pollute. It's only a question of how much. But, I think, with proper marketing and proper construction we're not going to pollute this area. What we're going to do is contribute to the pollution of the world.[15]

15. Reported in the *New York Times*, May 5, 1970.

This statement is by R. P. Clinton, president of the Clinton Oil Company; he not only said it in public, but confirmed it to reporters. This statement is not considered to be criminal, nor even crazy. The AEC also fosters global, rather than local, contamination by policies which permit a controlled level of radiation venting. How fragmented and abstract can we be and still survive?

Our only precedent for concerted action is military spending; the military-industrial complex has cost America more than $1.5 trillion since the *end* of World War II. Between today and 2000 we'll have to spend at least an equivalent amount on a social-industrial complex to schedule our future so it coincides with a year 2000 in which man is in balance with nature. Man has never been faced with this problem, and it will cost over $40 billion a year from now on to ensure our survival. Perhaps it isn't "fair" that the crisis came during our time, but it is here. The fear is that it will prove impossible to act in concert and perhaps we are too far in to get out now even if we began to coalesce. Yet while we try to fool or enlighten one another and as Congress debates the spending issue, the ocean keeps drawing out 11 million spilled gallons of oil higher into its food chain, to join the pesticide already there; the sky continues to darken and the black sunshine goes on shortening our lives as profit is maximized.

Three: Moving Society and Turning the Future

Action and Reaction Versus a Behavioral Laser

Even in the matter of survival, for every action there is an equal opposing reaction. In politics, the behavioral manifestation of the great law of energy provides the first Tuesday in November excitement; the same principle is also, however, a block to welding a unified ecological consciousness in the brief time we have to do so. Robert F. Kennedy liked to allude to two historical statements: one, the Chinese curse, "May you live in interesting times"; the other, an inscription carved on one of the blocks of the Great Pyramid, "No one cared enough to stop it."

Unless we care enough to overcome our political xenophobia, our ecological future will indeed be "interesting." Lasers obtain their incredible power because each separate light particle moves in the same direction and in step with all the others, as contrasted with a light bulb whose photons stream out randomly in all directions. Very little of the energy we are expending for survival has the coherence of a laser's beam; politics and suspicions so diffuse our total activity that the net result is that all forces balance each other out until the entire system is unable to move.

The behavioral crosscurrents on Earth Day in 1970 illustrated the tangle of opinions regarding unified efforts in behalf of the common environment. Although the odds were 365 to one against, April 22 was simultaneously Earth Day and Lenin's birthday. At least Earth Day missed Hitler's birthday by two days; still, many newspapers editorialized that this was no mere coincidence. The New York *Daily News* urged that we be not swayed by those forces which had so tipped their hand, forces which would have us weaken America by possibly jeopardizing the way we produce our oil and automobiles; big industry, the editorial assured us, will continue taking care of our interests in the future as it has done in the past. This, of course, was part of the reason Earth Day was needed in the first place.

The Daughters of the American Revolution declared not only that the day's activities were foreign-directed but that global pollution was "distorted and exaggerated by emotional declarations and by intensive propaganda." The survival motive had, as editorially expressed in the *New York Times*, "confronted for the first time those diehard opponents of change who will not be saved from a fire without suspiciously demanding to know where they are being taken and whether the danger of flames may not have been exaggerated for some sinister purpose." [1]

Industrialists expressed their peculiar view that they

1. May 25, 1970.

are somehow immune to environmental disaster. The director of air and water resources at the gigantic Union Camp paper mill in Savannah, Georgia—one of the area's major polluters—said:

People get extremely emotional about losing a species, but animals have been dying out every year clear back to the dinosaurs, and in most cases man had nothing to do with it. For that matter, it probably won't hurt mankind a whole hell of a lot in the long run if the whooping crane doesn't quite make it.[2]

Only a very limited understanding of extinction, the most chilly finality of all, would allow the phrase "doesn't quite make it," or ignore the fact that it is exactly our activities that are causing every extinction during our lifetime—which is why we worry about our own survival. Similarly anthropomorphic industrialists are, unfortunately, all too common.

There was also a regrettable feeling that concern for the environment would supersede concern for civil and economic rights of minorities. Mayor Carl B. Stokes decried the "glamour" in ecological involvement "at the expense of what the priorities of the country ought to be: proper housing, adequate food and clothing." Fortunately, the two movements are by no means mutually exclusive, and as it is the minorities who must often live in the poorest, most polluted, and most blighted environments. The two crusades can be joined, much as Cesar Chavez has done with pesticide spraying and the rights of the United Farm Workers' Union.

Many times, industry threatens to close down a polluting factory rather than pay to clean up its processes. Tacoma's acting city manager said that to him, the

2. Reported in the *New York Times*, May 25, 1970.

fumes from local smelters and pulp mills "smell like jobs." In some cases, workers have attacked students picketing their polluting factories on the grounds that their jobs are at stake and are more important than anti-pollution efforts. Officials of United States Steel, the world's second-largest steelmaker, threatened to shut down their huge Duluth plant if minimum air standards are enforced. The plant employs 2,000 people. Pulp mills dumping filth into the Columbia River System have also threatened to close if forced to clean up. In fact, some paper mills ran ads in the local newspapers suggesting that jobs are vital to the community, more than clean water. In some cases, small pulp mills might indeed be ruined if they had to spend money on antipollution; but just because they would go broke if they went clean, does this argue that they should therefore be allowed to continue pouring mercury and sulphite liquors into common waters? Even if it did, it would be no argument for U.S. Steel, a corporation which can certainly afford to be a "good neighbor" in any area where they operate a plant. For U.S. Steel to threaten workers in order to save private profits is an abuse of the private-ownership privilege.

It isn't difficult to sympathize with threatened workers, especially when many "activists" traduce the crisis in an endless circus of pranks and public spectacles. I spent the morning and afternoon of Earth Day speaking with residents of one of New York City's Phoenix Houses as part of their Earth Day program. The ex-heroin addicts, perhaps because they've faced the prospect of a poisoned future, spoke very seriously of the problems facing us; but what a contrast was encountered that night at the Fourteenth Street Earth Day celebration. Union Square had become a trashy, blaring carni-

val, littered with handbills and junk "sculpture," roaring
with amplified rock music and speakers tirading the excesses of society. Crowds queued in a long line to jam
into a plastic tent where the air was presumably cleaner.
The aura was eerie, almost surreal; a form of plague
dancing, the uncontrolled, lunatic celebrations which
took place during the medieval pandemics.

It may well be that rather than uniting young and
old, rich and poor, student and worker, the ecological
"movement" may drive them farther apart as each sus-
pects the other's motives, or accuses the other of excess,
as the common crisis deepens. The fundamental changes
required to break out of our trend could easily degenerate into backlash after backlash and never be accom-
plished.

Although the ecological crisis has been a media staple
for several years, consumer patterns haven't changed
noticeably. Boston supermarkets don't bother with products and packaging that pollute less because their sur-
veys indicate consumer indifference. There hasn't been
any rush to the unleaded gasolines. We discuss the problem, work to have a few laws passed, but don't really
change our own behavior. It is what we *actually do*
everyday, not just how we vote, which class of society
we blame, how "seriously" we accept the "radical ecologist's" urging. However much we're convinced" or
"alarmed" by the latest pollution special, it is what we
each *personally do* that is behind the problem or solution.

The indifference is sometimes agressively negative.
While our peril is indicated by rising mortality from
cancer and heart and lung disease, federal funds for
research in these areas have been cut to the minimum to
combat inflation. Many people were uneasy over the
growing degree to which Defense Department money

funded university research programs; the funding has been cut back, but no other money has flowed in, from HEW, for example, to fill the vacuum. The National Science Foundation can by no means absorb the research "orphans," and the net decline of scientific research at the university level is spreading as inflation drives more and more poorly funded activities out of existence. The danger is that we will retard intellectual, medical, technological, and *ecological* advancements, perhaps for decades. We depend to a major degree on the development of new knowledge; we have only learned enough to understand the true depth of our ignorance in chemistry, physics, engineering, education, biology, and—especially—ecology. We know enough only to be alarmed at what we have discovered, not nearly enough to understand how we may undo what previous ignorance has set into motion.

The growing antiscientific and anti-intellectual trend is alarming many scientists and other citizens. Astrology seems to satisfy within its pseudo science whatever "scientific" curiosity many of us have. Disciplined knowledge is of no value if it's dissolved in mysticism, yet a college degree was recently granted for the study of magic as an art and science. Many justify an anti-scientific bais on the grounds that so many scientific breakthroughs have backfired: DDT, cyclamates, leaky fission reaction, and the Bomb itself. These disasters could have been avoided, but not with less science, only with much *more* knowledge. Yet because of its abuses, many otherwise reasonable people have joined the churls and curmudgeons in advocating a moritorium or even an end to basic scientific research. To some, basic science is not only irresponsible, but irrelevant to pressing social needs: a waste of energy in "ivory tower" pursuits. To others, basic research is undesirable because it is too often manipulated by political and military goals: space, for example, or weaponry.

In many areas the view is truly tarnished, and if organizations such as the American Association for the Advancement of Science decry the hostility to pure research, they should investigate the corruptions of purity among their membership. The AAAS is not a censorship committee; nonetheless among scientists some moral control should be excercised over those working on the unbeatable military virus or antipersonnel electronics or even indestructable materials for containers. If scientists continue to be the pioneers of megadeath, high consumption and waste, and other technological abuses, the growing resentment against pure research will become justified.

Whether from calcified "patriotism," self-serving economics, minority impatience, "radical" clowning, habituated consumer, or antiscientific bias, the many actions and reactions rippling through society have so far kept us from moving in the direction of environmental balance. Society argues without moving.

They're Doing It in Sweden

Sweden seems to be leading the world in establishing an ecological national awareness and ending pollution. Scandinavians, perhaps owing to the rough climate, have traditionally had to take care of their land more than most people; the goal of the farmer is to leave the land richer for his having used it. This attitude alone provides a great head start, compared to American land management. The Swedes have proved quick to change; when the hazards of DDT and methyl mercury seed dressings were known, both were banned outright in Sweden. Both are still used here. The lead and sulphur content of fuels used in Sweden is now restricted, all automobiles have emission-control devices. Swedish industry must prove new facilities will not pollute before they can be built—a giant pulp mill was canceled because such proof couldn't be provided. The Swedish government has set strict pollution limits for all established industry, and will pay one-fourth the cost of required antipollution equipment.

During the next ten years, Sweden will allocate 5 percent of her total budget for environmental programs. Just think what a similar commitment could do in our country.

Sweden is as urbanized as America, but Scandanavian city dwellers have not forgotten the rural lakes and streams; when surveyed recently, nearly 70 percent said they would pay higher taxes to build sewage plants and other facilities to prevent pollution. During the past few years, the Swedish government has tripled the area of wildlife and nature preserves; in our country, nature preserves, even previously protected ones, are being lost year by year. It isn't merely the willingness to pay taxes, however; there is a carry-through of public commitment. Schoolchildren are taught about automobile pollution; more than 150,000 adults are taking night courses in environmental topics as part of a compulsory national education campaign.

Sweden fronts mainly on the Baltic sea and its Gulf of Bothnia. Because of a narrow access to the North Sea and the Atlantic, the Baltic changes water only every twenty-one years. It has become the most polluted sea in the world. Hydrogen sulphide, the indicator of anaerobic bacteria, tells of the absence of oxygen and the start of a biological desert at the lower levels of the sea. The fish are mercury-poisoned, the phosphate content of the Baltic has tripled since 1955. Swedish industry and government have joined forces to stop further pollution of the Baltic, and intense research is under way to determine methods of detoxifying the great sea.

Cleaning the sea as well as the air and land was the theme of an international antipollution trade show and conference held during Sweden's Earth Week in September, 1970. Earth Week attracted visitors from our own as well as European governments. Classes at Swedish schools were suspended and students urged to measure the pollution caused by smoke, chemicals, and noise. The example the Swedes have provided is clear—in fact, it is embarrassing.

In the long run, the Swedish initiative will be meaningless if the rest of us don't get moving. In the winter of 1969, thousands of dead sea birds began washing up on the shores of Northern Ireland, presumably killed by the high concentration of polychlorinated biphenol found in their tissues. PCB is an industrial chemical that disperses through food chains in a way similar to DDT. No one knows where the PCB is coming from, except that it comes from industry. Just as the acid rain and snow that falls over Sweden originates in Western Europe and the British Isles, it is possible that PCB and other, possibly more insidious, poisons are leaking back to ecologically aware Sweden from her ecologically unconscious neighbors.

As the world's prime polluter, we contribute the most to the degradation of the planet. But our few concrete moves are so timid compared to our waste power that we, too, are a net ecologically unconscious people. The

California coast is so contaminated with DDT and other pesticides that fish have been condemned for human consumption. Cormorants, grebes, and pelicans are vanishing—their food has made them unable to reproduce. Fish off the East Coast suffer fin rot, a pollution disease resembling leprosy—their fins are eaten away as they swim through the fouled ocean. The Navy recently dumped a vast amount of oil 50 miles from the Florida coast, where it is "legal" to dump, but great patches of oil formed a slick the size of Rhode Island and began moving onto 100 miles of prime Florida tourist beach: the Navy had to form an emergency task force to fight the invading oil. The Gulf of Mexico is again and again awash with oil, but it isn't the spectacular slicks which worry marine ecologists; rather the inexorable low-level oil pollution from boats and other everyday sources.

The automobile industry is now taking an activist stance on accusations that their products are polluters; a Chrysler Corporation executive denounced "frantic measures to over-control automotive emissions" brought on because "citizens have been needlessly frightened" by scare tactics. The President of General Motors says that pollution "cannot be legislated out of existence any more than the laws of nature," and the Ford Motor Company is sending a booklet, "Six Myths About Air Pollution and Your Automobile," to dealers so they can "explain" to customers.

The Hudson River beside New York City is crowded with typhoid, cholera, and diphtheria organisms thriving in raw sewage; every river bleeds America's poison into the sea, and almost all major rivers are septic. Because air and water are Earth's circulatory system, not even Sweden is safe unless her example inspires us to movement. No ecosystem is an island.

Start with a Stamp

Producing a change in the ecological inertia of the United States will be far more difficult and diverse a job than what has been done by Sweden, but it is still possible. Most of us would do something helpful if we were organized and knew how or what to do. The argument is over; we're all convinced that we'd better get in touch with the near future or we'll continue to live in a disintegrating present. The only question is where to begin.

Everyone's seen the public service announcements on late television which implore us to report air pollution violations locally and to write Clean Air, Washington, D.C. 20201. Public service advertising is among the most brilliant and creative stuff on television, but although its educational efficiency is high, I wonder how high its behavioral efficiency is. Have you actually sent a post card to Clean Air or any of the others requesting free further information? This is a good way to start. When the information arrives read it and try to follow through. Letter writing is important to the ecological and consumer movements because it is a concrete expression of opinion. If manufacturers and distributors of some product begin receiving letters from consumers who say they will not buy a product because of its ecological disadvantage, the maker or distributor will change the product rather than knowingly go broke. If we all stopped buying some brand, but didn't provide its maker with feedback as to *why* his product was losing sales, we may hurt his profits, but we aren't educating his industry. It should become routine to write such letters whenever appropriate.

For example, a catalog came in the mail from a mail order house specializing in soaps made in the "old fashioned way." The prose leader opens the catalog by mourning the passage of that cleaner age when air and water were pure and life could be enjoyed amid the harmonies of nature. It then went on to offer whale-oil soap and turtle-oil products. It has been estimated that one whale is killed every 12 minutes, mostly by Japanese and Russian whalers competing for the last of the now tiny herds; no sperm whale, it's said, ever dies of old age. Aside from whale meat eaten by the Japanese, these intelligent creatures go into pet food, perfume, transmission oil, and soap—none of which depend on the precious and rare whale. My wife returned the soap catalog, telling why, and requesting another catalog when the whale and turtle products were deleted. She later received a letter from the president of the firm explaining that whale-oil products had been deleted because of the opposition to their inclusion: other consumers had written and the company moved to eliminate at least its contribution to America's 30 percent of the world's whale market. But the "authentic, hard-to-come-by" Caribbean turtle-oil products have been expanded, although marine ecologists warn that sea turtles are in imminent danger. Because they all concentrate on a few small beaches to lay eggs, it only *appears* that there are many turtles.

The catalog, as well as her letter, were returned in the prepaid business reply envelope. These envelopes should always be used for the return of mail advertisements for offensive products. If you get junk mail for something so ecologically offensive as to prompt further action, urge your Congressman and Senators to broaden the protection against unsolicited sexually oriented junk mail to include any junk mail found offensive. Until you can legally be deleted from non-pornographic but none-theless offensive junk mailing lists, simply mailing the junk back first class in the prepaid envelope is sufficient. Scribble an explanation on it, if you wish. On the basis of paper waste alone, nearly all junk mail merits return; if it all came back at 8 cents an ounce, perhaps junk mailers would appreciate, if not their paper's value, at least its disposal problem.

Paying first-class postage for the return of junk mail is bad enough; paying for the receipt of someone else's junk mail is worse—stuff all the less offensive advertise-ments into the return envelope for the most offensive ad of the week, a kind of junk mail prize. If you don't think this type of thing is "fair," remember that mail advertising is only profitable because the low postal rates for junk mail are supported by high first-class rates. This subsidy, creating huge unnecessary paper consumption and solid waste, should be ended.

If, after a few days of return-envelope stuffing, you agree that junk mail is a source of waste, graduate to the next level of action: write your Representative and Senators. You need the name, but not the address—just House of Representatives or U.S. Senate, Washington, D.C. Complain about the volume of junk mail and ask your Congressman to support its limitation. A good habit to develop is writing a letter a month to a politician. If you learn that a Senator from another state is favoring action you agree with, write him. Politicians appreciate this kind of extra constituency. Senator Gaylord Nelson of Wisconsin recently proposed a fee on products whose packaging was not easily disposable—the money would go to local government for solid-waste programs. Senator Nelson's *Packaging Pollution Control Bill* is a good step; so is Senator Edmund Muskie's *Resource Recovery Bill*, which is a broader measure including demonstration projects for recycling and studies toward changing current packaging methods. Write your own representatives, urging their support of such measures.

Write a letter to the editor of your local paper as well, relating such measures to local needs—if it's printed, your action is *greatly* multiplied.

The Massachusetts Legislature recently amended the State Constitution to include the right of a citizen to an unpolluted environment. Does your state grant you such a right? Write your assemblyman or state senator to find out. If not, urge your support for such an amendment on the grounds that it provides a basis for antipollution suits.

Keep a copy of each letter and the reply in a general file; when your representatives send you status reports or ask your support, refer to past letters and promises. The best time for such "reminders" is, of course, near election. Use a broad yellow marker to highlight the environmental promises in campaign mailings and handouts; after the election, file the literature of the winner under Promises. It isn't hard to learn such tab-keeping, and being able to cast an environmentally wise vote more than makes up for the bother. Now that every politician is verbally proenvironment, keeping tabs on their actions is more important than ever: no one seeks office favoring air pollution, but too many later vote with industry against air standards.

It's hard to change daily routine and lifestyle to include ongoing ecological awareness and action, but if we can't change our behavior now, the results in only ten years will be forcing changes on us in unpleasant ways. Senator Clifford Case warns:

If a free people—who can do as they please—do not support reforms to protect their environment, which is their whole society, then out of necessity a police state will be born.

Senator Case isn't suggesting that uniformed police will search all grocery bags for nonreturnable bottles, but rather that if we cannot freely change our consumption and pollution behavior, dictatorial leadership from the top will have to impose changes to avert the inevitable disaster.

Using the mails is an important, basic method of identifying your existence and environmental concern; it is also an easy way to begin taking action:

1. Respond to public service antipollution ads. Be counted.
2. Write consumer letters to manufacturers or distributors—praise the good as well as boycott the bad.
3. Return or complain about excessive junk mail, all of it is just wastepaper and some of it promotes ecologically awful products.
4. Write letters to newspapers as well as politicians supporting environmentally sound legislation and urge them to initiate their own action.
5. Save politicians' mail-outs during and after election; keep aware of your representative's *actions*.

Five simple mailbox habits, but if you think they're too elementary or bothersome to maintain, you either underestimate their importance to an ecological lifestyle or aren't prepared to change your behavior so you actually *do* something that you didn't do before. Any amount of informed commitment is worthless if it produces no *act*.

After you've responded to a certain amount of public service ads and have been an environmental correspondent for a while, you'll notice more mailings coming your way from conservation and population groups. The good thing about this not-for-profit junk mail is the opportunity to join a local or short-term national campaign toward a specific goal. You've graduated from being a general correspondent to being a specific activist. At this point, you should consider joining a conservation group and supporting more specific projects. Below are some of the better known "basic" organizations. Write any or all of them—just a post card—saying that you are interested in learning more about what they stand for, what they are involved in, and so on. You'll get a lot of welcome mail as well as a bundle of fascinating information for free. You don't have to join any of them if you don't want to, of course, but when you learn of some of the brilliant things being done, and of the remarkable feats they've managed on behalf of all of us in the past years, you'll doubtless want to join at least one. Writing these groups for information should also spread your name to more mailing lists, getting you more involved in the growing network of mailbox activism. Send a card to each of these:

The Sierra Club
1050 Mills Tower
San Francisco, California 94104

Friends of Animals
11 West 60th Street
New York City 10023

The Wilderness Society
729 15th Street, N.W.
Washington, D.C. 20005

Friends of the Earth
30 East 42nd Street
New York City 10017

Zero Population Growth
367 State Street
Los Altos, California 94022

The Conservation Foundation
1250 Connecticut Avenue, N.W.
Washington, D.C. 20036

Scientists' Institute for Public Information
30 East 68th Street
New York City 10021

National Audubon Society
1130 5th Avenue
New York City 10028

Planned Parenthood/World Population
515 Madison Avenue
New York City 10022

The Izaak Walton League
1326 Waukegan Road
Glenview, Illinois 60025

The Nature Conservancy
1522 K Street, N.W.
Washington, D.C. 20005

Send a card to each now before first-class postage goes up again; 55 cents and 30 minutes will bring a wealth of information and chances for action. Not all the groups are strictly conservation; Friends of Animals works not only for wildlife but humane legislation for domestic and research animals. The Conservation Foundation can send you lists of action groups in your state. Planned Parenthood and Zero Population Growth obviously stress the population aspect. Friends of the Earth may be somewhat more activist than the Audubon Society or even the Sierra Club, from which it emerged.

Not all groups are clubs—that is, one doesn't join and pay dues. Contact each of them, then sit back and find out which is which and how many you can support. They're all eager to hear from you.

Many of the clubs publish periodicals. The *Sierra Club Bulletin* and *Audubon Magazine* are perhaps most famous, but *Izaak Walton Magazine* and *The Living Wilderness* (Wilderness Society) are among others, all of which are excellent. As long as you are writing to groups, also write the following ecologically oriented periodicals for information and subscription rates:

Environment
Committee for Environmental Information
438 North Skinker Blvd.
St. Louis, Missouri 63130

Natural History
American Museum of Natural History
79th Street & Central Park West
New York City 10024

National Parks Magazine
1300 New Hampshire Avenue, N.W.
Washington, D.C. 20036

National Wildlife Magazine
National Wildlife Federation

1412 16th Street, N.W.
Washington, D.C. 20036

Prevention
Prevention Magazine
Emmaus, Pennsylvania 18049

Population Bulletin
Population Reference Bureau
1755 Massachusetts Avenue
Washington, D.C. 20036

Like the groups listed, the magazines vary in their approach and emphasis. *Environment* magazine gives the latest in responsible ecological muckraking; *Prevention* provides consumer tip-offs and explores safety hazards; *Natural History* is wildlife, fascinating and beautiful. All the magazines are excellent sources of current information and provide means for reader involvement. Send for a mailer from each one.

For in-depth information on ecological lifestyles, look into:

The Mother Earth News
P.O. Box 38
Madison, Ohio

Subscribing to magazines and investigating and joining conservation groups are not in themselves action, but means of getting information and opportunities to act. Subscription and dues payments hardly absolve you from your mailbox chores—they will, in fact, give you more chores. To an extent, numerical weight of membership gives organizations great clout: the 80,000 members of the Sierra Club give that daddy of them all great authority before government and industry. An ecological lifestyle, however, requires much more than carefully reading each month's magazines and sending off a few good letters.

Local Action Groups

There may be a college somewhere in the United States whose campus has no environmental action group, but it's a good bet to contact the nearest college and/or university's information center or student newspaper to find out what's going on in your area. Don't omit smaller branches of the state university or private schools. Check the phone book. If your town has no educational unit above high school, look into the high school programs. High school students are surprisingly more active and aware about the condition of the world they will have to live in than many people think—they have to be.

If you're in school, and there aren't several groups to join, you can start one. The greatest need for high school action is probably in small rural towns far from university campuses but in the center of thoughtless pesticide and predator-control programs. Few small towns have better than simple open dumps for waste disposal. Sciences teachers, especially biology teachers, can be sources of information, but don't ignore the groups previously listed. In this case, mentioning that you're a student works in your favor.

If you're already a member of a civic, service, social, or church group, environmental action should certainly be one of its commitments. Does your group have a doctor or teacher who could discuss the hazards posed

by local polluters? Is there a lawyer or law student who
might describe class action suits? Have you discussed
joining with other groups, including students, to promote
common causes such as recycling centers or trash-re-
demption facilities? If you are a member of a social or
civic group that hasn't made any commitments for
environmental action, invite student speakers from a
nearby university or high school group.

For information on forming community action on
behalf of the environment, write:

> Citizens's Advisory Committee
> 1700 Pennsylvania Avenue, N.W.
> Washington, D.C. 20006

Once you begin noticing them, projects for your
group to consider will be plentiful. Public service
advertisements alone provide enough preliminary information to get started; unfortunately, the stations tend
to discharge their obligation to run the ads by concentrating them in time spots undesirable for commercial
advertising—such as early morning or late night. This
alone is something for action: persuade your local station
to put on a few more of these ads during prime time.

In small towns and suburbs, neighborhood groups of
even three or four families can combine lot space for a
garden, and buy and use power mowers in common.
Dormitory groups in schools, and tenant associations in
apartment buildings, can provide a constant and informed
pressure on city officials and politicians, as well as joining with regular civic and school environment groups.

Even if you aren't part of a reguarly meeting group,
involve your circle of friends. If you subscribe to one
of the magazines or receive bulletins from national
groups, lend these to your friends and have an ecology

party a week later. You might show a film, free from a library or university or rented through a conservation group. If you are a photographer, show slides depicting local pollution outrages. Send a really prize photo to your newspaper.

Court action is rapidly becoming one of the most effective environmental moves. The Sierra Club has gone to court against the Department of Agriculture and the Forest Service to halt the sale and cutting of one million acres in Alaska's Tongass National Forest. This sale is the third one of Tongass timber and violates, according to the Sierra Club, forest management principles of sustained or perpetual yield.

Fifteen states are suing before the U.S. Supreme Court to compel the Big Three auto manufacturers to install pollution control devices on all cars they built during the past seventeen years, when they allegedly conspired to suppress the development of such devices.

The Environmental Defense Fund, P.O. Box 238, Brookhaven, New York 11719, pioneered in well-known cases against DDT and other pesticides. This group is now working on bringing to court major industries polluting New York City's air, claiming that they contribute substantially to 10,000 deaths each year.

Because of extensive court action against polluters, Los Angeles reportedly has the cleanest industrial base in the country. The city has filed more than 4,000 criminal suits, winning 90 percent. L.A. is still heavily polluted with the lead miasma from ethyl gasolines—soil in Los Angeles parks contains 3,000 parts per million of lead, compared with 1,900 parts per million in Moscow, where leaded gas isn't used. New York City, with far less exposed soil, has doubtlessly as much lead as L.A. Friends of the Earth, noting the hazards of pollution from oversized engines and leaded gasoline, appealed to WNBC in New York for application of the "fairness doctrine," which holds TV stations responsible for presenting time for opposing views on controversial issues. FOE cites as precedent the case made in 1966 by John F. Bamzhaf III, which resulted in the TV commercials against smoking. WNBC responded as expected: in their view advertisements for big cars and leaded gas don't constitute a controversial issue. FOE will appeal to the Federal Communications Commission, which is what happened in the smoking case.

Industry and, unfortunately, the Justice Department recognize the implications of possible court action by consumer and environment groups and are moving to make citizen suits more difficult. The Internal Revenue Service is working to end the tax exemption of such groups—contributions, no longer tax deductible, could dry up.

The Justice Department is advising United States attorneys to prosecute water polluters under the 1965 Water Pollution Control Act, rather than the Refuse Act of 1899. Under the Refuse Act, a citizen or group need only provide the U.S. Attorney with evidence (photos, witnesses) of a factory polluting a navigable waterway and the attorney can sue. Fines from $500 to $2,500 a day—as well as a jail sentence of up to one year—can be imposed. Half the fine goes to whoever provided the evidence. Conservationists feel the Justice Department opposes the 1899 act because it gives too much power to the people. It also allows the citizen (or his group) to press the suit in his own name if the U.S. attorney will not.

Senators Hart and McGovern have introduced a bill to guarantee a citizen's right to sue on behalf of his environment. The Justice Department opposes this, claiming that only experts in administrative agencies have legal standing before federal courts.

Even if your group is not yet ready to enjoin legal action, you should certainly move to preserve your right to do so in the future. Contact your Senators and Congressman and urge their support of the Hart-McGovern "citizen suit" bill. Also urge their support for applying the fairness doctrine to damaging products other than cigarettes.

Although the number of environmental lawsuits is said to be doubling every six months, the time required to decide them remains long, and issues after issues emerge which require immediate action. How many of the following areas do you think need immediate attention?

1. Although 80 percent of us live where mass transit is badly needed, highways get sixteen times as much money as mass transit. Aside from causing 60 percent of the dirty air (80 percent in some cities), the spread of concrete is smothering greenery at the rate of 2 million acres a year, and is paid for by the Highway Trust Fund, fed by gasoline and automotive taxes. Why not move some of this money into impacted mass transit?

2. If you live in a city where high-rise steel buildings are going up, you doubtlessly have asbestos in your lung tissue. It is cheaper to fireproof a building by spraying its supporting members with asbestos and water, rather than by encasing them in concrete. Fifty percent of the asbestos escapes as a fine dust into the environment. Once inhaled, the tiny particles are never "flushed out" of the lungs, but break into smaller and smaller subcellular particles, which have been shown to cause lung cancer. Cheap substitutes such as rockwool and fiberglass have similar drawbacks. Work for a city ordinance

forbidding all such spraying. Include regulations against unmuffled compressors and your ears as well as lungs will get some relief.

3. Each year $300 million worth of sulphur goes into the air as waste sulphur dioxide. It only costs $7 a ton to reclaim this sulphur, and it's worth up to $10 a ton on the industrial market. Sulphur is a short-supply material; we waste as much as we mine each year. Local municipal regulations should be established requiring sulphur-burning industries to use profit-making stack cleaners. This would combine profits, recycling, and less poisonous air.

4. Charles F. Luce, chairman of Consolidated Edison in New York, proposed a national tax on consumer utility bills to fund industry research for new methods of generating electricity. Public utilities have put up $37 million for such research; firms such as General Electric and Westinghouse have put up about $105 million. Luce says that another $200 million is needed, and feels that those who will benefit—you and me—should bear this burden. An alternative view is that private utilities benefit from power consumption in the form of profits and that it is less than fair that we pay for research while private profits remain untouched. Your group might pass their sentiments along to:

Power Companies
1345 Avenue of the Americas
New York City 10019

This is the address of the private utilities combine which runs all those ads urging the desirability of atomic-fired power generation—research and insurance for which are subsidized with our tax money.

5. Fossil-fired power generation wouldn't be as ex-

pensive if low-sulphur import gas and oil were available to utilities. Because of the oil-import quota, however, utility (as well as consumer) prices for fuel are unnaturally high. If import fuel could be used by utilities, perhaps the money saved could be earmarked for clean-energy research. This is not to say that the door would be opened for national consumer use of lower-cost foreign oil and gas (although many feel it ought to be), only for exemption from the quota to allow the cheaper clean fuel to utilities, provided they used the price reduction for research, not profit. You might suggest this not only to your federal representatives, but to:

American Gas Association, Inc.
605 Third Avenue
New York City 10016

American Petroleum Institute
1271 Avenue of the Americas
New York City 10020

6. If you are active in church affairs, suggest a sermon or discussion on the role of Christianity in environmental abuse and pollution. The School of Theology at Claremont, California, held a symposium recently on the "theology of survival." The view was that traditional church attitudes sanction environmental exploitation by their definition of man as dominant in nature, and that such precepts must be changed.

7. If you're active in university affairs, enlist the aid of economics or law students to investigate stocks held by your school. Campaigns are being waged on several major campuses to have the university vote its stock on behalf of consumer and environmental efforts.

8. If your group believes that products should be

manufactured and marketed with recycling or reuse considerations designed in, write to:

National Association of Manufacturers
277 Park Avenue
New York City 10017

Association of General Merchandise Chains, Inc.
1441 Broadway
New York City

9. The concept behind the FCC "fairness doctrine" should extend to all advertising in any media. The advertising industry does good with their public service spots, but more could be done. Billboards could urge motorists to recycle and not to throw cans out the window. Beer advertisers could include a "recycle me" plea on their labels. Advertising in general is getting a black eye for its role in promoting senseless consumption; a campaign for recycling by the advertising industry could serve them as excellent public relations. Write to:

Association of National Advertisers
155 East 44th Street
New York City 10017

American Association of Advertising Agencies
200 Park Avenue
New York City 10017

Institute of Outdoor Advertising
625 Madison Avenue,
New York City

Friends of Animals provides multiple copies of their most powerful printed ads on behalf of animals. FOA also provides mats for their ads in various sizes for groups to print in their local paper. Until the industry itself comes around, FOA is the best source for ecological advertising. Their mailings are also excellent; you should be on their list.

Last but hardly least is the type of local action one need not have a group perform. Example: Mayor John Lindsay of New York hopped out of a station wagon one winter day in 1967, picked up a cigarette wrapper tossed from a truck, ran up to the truck, and threw it at the three men inside, saying, "I'm the Mayor. I'm trying to keep the city clean. You ought to be ashamed of yourselves." The stunned litterbugs merely muttered, "Yes, sir."

Granted, had John Lindsay been a long-haired student he might well have been pummeled for his efforts; still, environmental action means moving whenever it is possible. The same can be done by us by simply saying, "Excuse me, but I think you dropped this." Returning litter to those who "lose" it might aggregate into a meaningful group action after all.

The ultimate in individual action is The Fox of Kane County, Illinois, west of Chicago. An environmental Zorro who leaves notes explaining his action, the mystery figure dumps sewage on the floors of polluting industry, clogs factory waste outlets which poison rivers, and for the past few years has been eluding law-enforcement agencies. No one is suggesting emulating this activity, but it has at least produced some changes, and bumper stickers have appeared reading "Go Fox—Stop Pollution."

Four: Feeding the Family

Food Action No. 1: Clean It Up

". . . in the United States there is a spreading revolt by women against technology which orders their lives. . . . That revolt could throw off base the consumer industries where growth is based on planned steadily increasing consumption by docile housewives."
—James Ridgeway, *The Politics of Ecology*

Apart from lowering personal consumption of animal protein, we should insist that the Food and Drug Administration be properly funded and staffed to do its job. Other problems with the FDA involves its bureaucratic spirit—an example is the recent demotion of an FDA scientist who protested the nonscientific editing of laboratory research. This manipulated data permitted cyclamates on the market in spite of evidence that they are carcinogens. This casts a serious doubt over every FDA "safety standard" for pesticides and other residues, as well as their rulings on chemical preservatives, dyes, medicines, and other agents.

Imagine the situation where the world's richest and most resourceful government cannot protect its citizens not only from the traditional food hazards but also from new ones being added to foods with seemingly every new product that appears. Certainly, if it were some foreign nation, rather than our own farmers and merchants, who posed even one percent of this hazard, we would long ago have settled the matter—if necessary, by war.

Obviously, it is more important that our food be well-inspected as the environment fills with contamination, but of the 1.6 billion pounds of meat imported each year, less than one percent is inspected. Only 10 percent of domestically produced meat is inspected. Fish are inspected only by a few industry-salaried agents. Yet 40 percent of all communicable disease comes to us through food.

The FDA shares meat and poultry regulations with the Department of Agriculture. For some time now, the poultry industry has been deploring the "waste" of 2 million chickens a month (one percent of the monthly slaughter) simply because the birds have visible avian leukosis, a cancer. The industry claimed in its 1970 campaign that what was taken for cancer was often only large pimples, but that even if it were cancer, there was no proof that whatever caused cancer in the chicken would cause it in humans eating the lesions. As we know so little of cancer, this could be true—or false. The lesions could be cut off, diverted to pet food, and the remainder sold for human consumption. Frighteningly enough, an advisory committee of the Department of Agriculture agreed with the industry. Fortunately, Secretary of Agriculture Clifford M. Hardin declined to allow such chickens on the market. Presumably, the industry will try again, when there is a new Secretary.[1]

Actually, there is a precedent for allowing the sale of cancerous chickens: for over sixty years, Americans have been eating millions of pounds of beef from cattle infected with "cancer eye" and other tumors. Department of Agriculture policy for cattle holds that if the tumor itself is cut out, the rest of the carcass may be sold for human consumption; Americans ate 103,000 such carcasses in 1969, approximately one percent of the total amount of cattle marketed. This policy is now under review.

Although the Federal Meat Inspection Act of 1967 required, by law, all meat sold within every state to meet inspection standards equivalent to those for interstate meat shipments, only fourteen states met the law's December 15, 1970, deadline—and this deadline had been extended one full year beyond that specified. Thirty-five states are lagging in coming up to standard. Another extension is being granted, which Ralph Nader has termed a violation of the law. According to the Act, states failing to come up to standards by deadline would have their inspection facilities taken over by federal officials, but the Department of Agriculture apparently will not enforce the full measure of the law.

On the average, two food products a week are recalled, usually by manufacturers, sometimes by the FDA. The products are ordered off the market for containing mercury, splinters of glass, insect or rodent particles and/or feces, salmonella infestation, and sometimes even botulism, the deadliest toxin on earth. Only 10 percent of the

1. Reported in the *New York Times*, February 5, 1970.

fish spawning in the sewage slime and industrially coastal waters are ever inspected, and even then, the inspectors work for the fishermen, not the public.

The pesticides are everywhere; in one series of tests, the FDA found nearly 50 percent of 49,000 tested food samples to contain residue of pesticides, and 3 percent of the samples showed residues above even the FDA limitations, which have themselves been challenged as inadequate. Meats and fish were highest, eggs and dairy products next highest, and fruits and vegetables most likely to be within limits. It is advisable not to eat any wild game or fish, even inland fresh-water fish; the fish and game birds of many parts of North America are reported dangerously high in mercury, and many wild animals—deer, for instance—contain pesticide residues well above anything the FDA would ever allow.

American women have been found to contain in their breast milk up to 5 times the maximum DDT concentrations permitted for dairy milk; women contemplating breast feeding should have their milk tested first.

The developing fetus accumulates an increasing burden of pesticide as it forms; to then expose the baby to a DDT dose possibly 5 times greater than it would normally receive otherwise may be too great to permit breast feeding in ignorance. University of Missouri scientists have shown DDT to increase the presence of chemicals in the liver which in turn reduce the amount of estrogen in the bloodstream. Estrogen is the key to birth control pills, and their effectiveness might be destroyed by long-term exposure to DDT. Estrogen is the hormone which controls female sexual development; what constant, chronic deprivation of this hormone might mean to a child exposed to DDT in the womb, at the breast, and at every mealtime thereafter is unknown.

We have been all used as guinea pigs in the great experiment with preservatives, thickeners, dyes, bleaches, emulsifiers, flavorings, buffers, stabilizers, sequestrants, surfactants—the whole list of 3,000 intended additives having nothing whatsoever to do with nutrition. We not only lead the world in chemicalized food, but also in degenerative disease, and have no idea where the exact relationship between the two lies.

About the only defense we have at the consumer level is to read the label. Washing vegetables and fruits helps, although pesticides are not only on the skin of the food, but throughout it, taken into the cell with water.

For more information on food safety and food danger, write:

Scientist's Institute for Public Information
30 East 68th Street
New York City 10021

United Farm Workers Union
275 Seventh Avenue
New York City 10001

If you would like to complain about the "cancer eye" policy or applaud the ban on cancerous chicken, write:

U.S. Department of Agriculture
Consumer Protection
26 Federal Plaza
New York City

You may also write the USDA in Washington, D.C.

Find out what agencies in your state are responsible for inspecting state-produced food, and ask what inspection and regulation programs are under way. In New York, address all inquiries to:

New York State Department of Agriculture and
   Markets Food Control
93 Worth Street
New York City 10013

In other states, write State Department of Agriculture,
care of the State Capitol. You may receive a lot of
pamphlets and mail-outs which perhaps won't answer
any of your questions satisfactorily, but at least *they'll*
know that yet another person is alert to their existence.

How many of the 19 million hapless creatures slaughtered and sold with no federal inspection found their way
to your table last year? Buying name brands from
major supermarket chains is no assurance of clean meat;
Ruth Winter mentions that meats sold by Safeway, A&P,
Piggly-Wiggly, Kroger, and First National have been
proved contaminated, even when carrying prestigious
brand labels such as Armour and Swift.[2]

No one wants to sell you unsafe food, although it seems
often that industry wouldn't mind moving us a bit closer
to the line. The problem is lack of inspection. Ohio has
five inspectors; Maryland has three. How many in your
state? You have a right to know. Of all the food fouled
with insect or rodent parts and feces or chemical residues above safety limits, only 10 percent is stopped by
the FDA.

You've been eating the rest.

2. Ruth Winter, *Poisons in Your Food* (New York: Crown,
1969) pp. 77–96.

Food Action No. 2: Buy Less of It

If present inflation continues, the over-all cost of food will be 3 times greater in 2000 than today. Although this seems a sufficiently miserable prospect, food costs may in reality be much greater.

The greatest rises in food prices have not gone to the farmer or rancher, but to the processor, distributor, and retailer, whose technological and labor costs are governed by social and economic trends far removed from the field or range. As the trend to depletion of mineral, forest, and fossil resources increases, general economics will have even more influence on the cost of food than will the fertility of Iowa and California. Inflation may not be so "easily" dealt with as in the past, and food prices may climb until the year 2000 results in costs which would drive today's one-way superconsumers to hair shirts and brown rice. Still, even if food were free, environmental reasons alone urge that we pare down the weight of our grocery bag.

If you live in an area where there are still family-operated farms, and if you like to take drives into the country, stop at a farmhouse and ask if anyone in the area sells vegetables, eggs, milk, or fruit. You may be able to make a good contact right there for much cheap, in-season produce. Most farmers don't mind selling directly to the consumer. You have the double benefit of saving money and getting fresh, unpackaged items. If your farm contact believes in growing food organically, or even "semiorganically," you have the further advantage of knowing your total intake of pesticide and other residues is at least that much lower.

Growing your own food and preserving it is the best method for cutting costs and improving nutrition. Even if you cannot grow your own, you can still preserve food bought from the farm. The Department of Agriculture and the U.S. Government Printing Office regularly issue bulletins on food preservation; write for them.

Good supermarket habits can also cut costs. Make as few market trips as possible, but always take a list with you and *follow it*. If you go to market by car, don't use all that polluting horsepower just to haul yourself—take a friend. Don't shop together, however; going through the aisles encourages impulse buying. To also combat impulse buying, *never shop when hungry*. Americans tend to overeat by an estimated 30 percent; hungry shoppers buy more than satiated ones.

Take a market basket, string bag, or shopping bag, as is generally done in Europe, and ask that your purchases be packed in your own bag. Try to avoid brown paper grocery bags unless you know you can give them another use before they hit the solid waste pile. Buy large amounts of staple foods, and decant them into smaller containers for home use. If you can get a food freezer and a blender, do so. Buy "day-old" bread at the bakery, freeze and thaw it—it will taste fresh. Name-brand foods are costly because of their advertising. Avoid them, whenever possible, for the store's "house brand," usually the same product sold more cheaply.

If you wish to be a secret activist, carry a pack of index cards and a marker with you. If you discover whale meat listed on a brand of pet food, secretly leave a little note in the display to advise other shoppers of this ecological incongruity. While up to 20 million people starve each year. America put one-third of its fish into pet food. Unless your point is obvious, give a source for your information. During the legendary grape boycott, one supermarket in my area continually had its grape displays ticketed in this manner; eventually, it discontinued selling them.

Read the food ads in your local paper; usually they all appear on one day; shop these sales, buy loss-leaders and freeze or otherwise store them. Keep a record of what you normally pay for basic items to help you judge the value of sales. Set a limit on how much you will spend, and exceed it *only* if you discover a basic food on sale. Until we bring about unit pricing, it is a difficult piece of arithmetic to determine if one brand's 13 ounces of something for 79 cents is a better deal than 9½ ounces of another brand at two for 99 cents.

If your store gives trading stamps, change stores. The stamps are not free and are not a "bonus." If they were, the stamp companies would not be rich. If you are offered the stamps, always take them. If you take them, use them—unused stamps are simply free profit for the stamp company. If you don't want to bother with the stamps, find an environment group or church or social club which will use them.

The bottling industry is gearing up to fulfill its own prediction of 216 billion bottles during the 1970s; make it hot for them by buying only returnable bottles. A man in Sydney, Australia, was fined $60 for pitching a bottle from his car; if we had such an environmental sense of law and order, we wouldn't face the prospect of an avalanche of throwaways. Besides, look at the average economics involved (cola is the example):

.85 cents an ounce in a 16 ounce returnable bottle
1.02 " " " " " " " disposable bottle
1.36 " " " " " 12 " aluminum can

This means that the joy of adding another bottle to the solid-waste problem costs you 2 cents; the aluminum can 6.12 cents. You also pay a bit for the cardboard wrapper for the cans and for the paper bag. You'll be charged for the bag even if you don't use one, but you can save the environment a lot by buying returnable bottles and asking for a cardboard box—the store has the boxes anyway, and they're stronger than bags; they make good trash or garbage containers.

Avis Ogilvy of the Sierra Club suggests making copies of the following and giving them to merchants and shoppers:

Many members of the Sierra Club and of Friends of the Earth, as well as other concerned individuals, are helping beat the growing problem of waste disposal by avoiding unnecessary wrapping and onetime-use containers. In my shopping, I have pledged to give preference to returnable bottles, merchandise with single, not multiple wrapping, etc. Won't you help by stocking and prominently displaying this kind?

Political action you or your group supports should include limiting the tax deduction food companies now enjoy for the research and development of ever-more competitive packaging. We're paying on both ends as long as it is tax deductible.

Perhaps the most profound change to become more ecologically responsible requires deadvertising the American meat myth. This is part of our cultural kit; those not complying with it are considered to be "religious" or, less politely, "eccentric."

American carnivorism is in total the most intense in the world. On a per capita basis we consume over 185 pounds of red flesh annually. In terms of all types of meat, our yearly demand of 237 pounds is the world's record. Red meat, like all animal protein, certainly has nutrition value, but the level at which we maintain our flesh fetish goes well beyond science and nutrition and into cultural self-image. Most adult males demand steak for the same reason they drive muscle cars.

Food Action No. 3: Kitchen Conservation

The rise of kitchen inefficiency, termed "convenience," is an area in which we can do much to cut personal consumption and waste.

Good kitchen hands know many ways of conserving food, chief among them the ability to cook. For example, buying prepared potato products means that up to 50 percent of the potatoes you finally use were wasted at the factory. Potatoes are a cheap source of vitamins and minerals and are not as fattening as most people think. Boil them with the skins on to preserve vitamins and minerals (this rule applies for most thin-skinned vegetables). Cover the pot, use as little water as possible, and when the vegetables are done, use the nutrient-loaded water for mashed potatoes, soup, or gravy base. Don't boil vegetables until they're mush; they should be just somewhat crisp.

Many foods should be served raw whenever possible. Apples contain valuable pectin in their peel. Raw carrots are much tastier and better for the teeth, and their roughage aids digestion.

A seemingly endless chain of empty baby-food jars can be avoided (as well as whatever extra salt or MSG may be involved) by churning adult food (unseasoned) in a blender. Be sure to check with your pediatrician before planning your infant's menu.

If you drink buttermilk, clabber your own by mixing up a quart jar of powdered milk, adding a half cup of buttermilk and letting it stand until it all becomes buttermilk. Save some as starter for the next quart, and you've ended a chain of milk cartons.

Residents on Manhattan's West Side have not only opened collection sites for recycling but have also begun forming food-buying cooperatives. Such ventures are also emerging on college campuses and are appropriate for suburbanites as well. Distributors are usually willing to sell to these cooperatives on a case-lot basis somewhat above wholesale but much less than retail. A nominal initiation fee, such as $10, is usually asked to meet operating costs; some cooperatives will allow you to be a semi-participating member: when they make a particularly good buy they call you to help absorb their surplus. Even if you cannot join a formal cooperative, try to combine a few neighbors and buy big bags of flour, sugar, rice, legumes, and other staples—even buying at retail will save if the bag-size is large enough.

Store your staples in bugproof containers to avoid insects or, worse, not finding the salmonella they may have tracked in.

The only way to fight cockroaches is to keep them from food and water. Spraying will only dent their numbers unless you dismantle your entire house. Never use a vaporizing pest strip; no-pest strips have had an unseemly developmental history which included fighting the government over the label warning. The warning is there now, but what it doesn't mention is that food will absorb the vaporized poison from the air. Avoid them entirely; use a strip of flypaper and a swatter. The safest insecticides are dry, such as the silica desiccant powders, or those made of only natural ingredients, such as pyrethrins (be sure the label indicates no complex chemicals as propelling media—"Hargate's" uses only mineral and sesame oil). Cut off the bug's water supply by fixing all leaking faucets. If a natural ingredient pesticide is not available in your area, contact the supplier of Hargate's Natural Ingredient Insecticide:

Mylen Co.
230 East 25th Street
New York City 10010

For a nonpoisonous desiccant powdered spray, SG-57-Plus can be ordered from:

X-Pest Control
120 Liberty Street
New York City 10006

Mice are fierce insectivores which will, if they have no other food, keep a tight rein on your insect population. Unfortunately mice do have their drawbacks, and if you'd like to be rid of them, don't put out poison, which draws them, but mothballs. This will soon cause them to decamp, at which point you plug their portholes with steel wool. The odor of a cat will also work. Once they realize there is danger, they will often all move on.

Rats, however, are among man's deadliest enemies, and if you have them, spare no expense; in New York City there is at least one rat for every resident, and, like the fabled rats of Hamelin, they fight the cats. Professional extermination is probably your only real defense.

Assuming that your communally purchased flour is safe from bugs, the next step is using it to avoid packaging and additives by baking bread. There are many recipes for basic bread—Sylvia Van Sickle donated the following for a simple, low-cost, super-protein version of country farm bread.

It is "flexible" because it can be streamlined, to include dry milk solids, vegetable oil or margarine but no egg—or it can be enriched, to include whole milk, butter, egg, and wheat germ, even brewer's yeast or soy flour. The dozen rolls or two small loaves will come out crusty, golden and fragrant, whichever method you use. Optional ingredients are in parentheses.

Flexible Bread

1 package dry yeast
1 tablespoon sugar or honey
1 teaspoon salt
2 tablespoons vegetable oil *or* soft margarine *or* butter
(1 whole egg)
(¼ cup wheat germ)
(2 tablespoons soy flour or brewer's yeast)
½ cup dry milk solids + 1 cup hot water *or* ½ cup
    whole milk + ½ cup hot water
3–4 Heckers unbleached flour *or* fresh, stone-ground
    wheat flour

Preheat oven to 400°. Combine first set of ingredients, mixing well. Add milk (dry or whole) and water, mixing well. Add flour a cup at a time, mixing well, until dough pulls from side of bowl and can be formed into a ball for kneading. Turn dough out on lightly floured board and knead until smooth, elastic, shiny. Put into lightly oiled, deep dish; lightly oil top of dough; place inverted plastic bag over top of bowl, tucking ends under bowl and leaving a dome about the same size again as the bowl for humid, draft-free rising. Let rise at least an hour, or until doubled in bulk. Form the dough into loaves or rolls at this point; or punch down and let rise another hour for extra fluffy bread and rolls. To form into two small loaves, divide dough, roll out into an oblong shape about a half inch thick. Roll up jellyroll fashion, tucking ends and "seam" under. Place on baking sheet. Oil top lightly, slash with knife on top for decorative crust. Repeat for second loaf. For rolls, divide dough into 10 or 12 pieces and follow same procedure. Bake 25 to 35 minutes. Remove at once to cool. (For fresh baked bread or rolls to serve guests, make up loaves or rolls before hand; place them in the refrigerator and chill until ready to bake, from 2 to 24 hours ahead. You can pop the dough into the oven as guests arrive.

Other than cooking, washing is the major kitchen activity. Use washing and baking soda in place of more potent commercial powdered cleansers. The sodas will not work as fast as the heavy-duty cleansers, but for 80 percent of the routine cleaning, they work fine and cut down on the flow of chemicals from your sink to your nearest river or lake.

Garbage "disposal" units built into the sink increase by one-fourth the load on your septic tank or sewage treatment. They are banned in New York City, and should be used only in areas where garbage dumps are terrible and sewage treatment is wonderful—an unlikely combination. Food wastes optimally should be composted, but putting them in watertight containers (coffee cans, plastic bags) and out with the solid waste is much better than adding them to lakes and rivers now dying because of organic refuse. The grinder is also a source of noise pollution, generally operating at 90 decibels, well above "safe" limits. And, of course, they consume electricity.

The garbage grinder doesn't use nearly as much power as an automatic dishwasher, which uses every "average" day enough power to burn a 100-watt bulb for ten hours. If the dishwasher has a "sanitation" or superheated cycle, you're consuming much more energy needlessly—turn it off before it goes into this cycle, let the dishes drip dry.

If you don't have an automatic dishwasher, you save electricity, hot water, and phosphate detergent. Generally, all dishwashing detergent for automatics is *high* in phosphate; all detergent for hand dishwashing is *low* in phosphate. Dishwashing liquids such as Lux and Dove and Ivory and Joy and Trend contain no phosphates. Just fill up the sink with dishes, pour in a capful of liquid (always measure, otherwise you use more than you think), let the sink fill with hot water—and walk away, returning to drain the sink and rinse the dishes after the water is warm. Don't let water run as you wash—you'll waste up to 30 gallons each time.

Dilute your dishwashing liquid half-and-half with warm. Then use the same amount and see if it doesn't work just as well. When the bottle is empty, slosh it out with warm water and you'll get one more sink's worth of dishwashing. If the water feels "slippery" between your fingers, you have enough soap. We generally use much more soap than we need. Hold the day's dishes so they can all be washed at once. If you use soap pads, cut them into quarters. Keep them in water (in a small jar) when not in use; the water absorbs the soap and recharges the pad when it's returned to the jar.

Save scraps of hand soap in a container; from time to time, put warm water over the scraps to "melt" them, then use the liquid for dish or hand washing; it works just about as well as the dishwashing liquid.

Five: Preventing Solid Waste by Saving Money

Reusing Containers—Metal and Glass

In the supermarket, drugstore or dimestore stands a large, brightly colored pasteboard and paper display of cards; each card sprouts a stiff, clear plastic bubble containing a plastic film-wrapped small box; within the box is a styrofoam case enclosing a tiny bottle with label, cap, and a fluff of cotton fills half the bottle which holds—what? Even if we avoid such blatant overwrapped packages, there will still be a steady flow of metal, glass, plastic, and paper disposable containers through our lives.

Do these materials come into our house, get used once, and then flow out to join the flood of solid waste? Or do the containers tarry awhile, put to a new use which prevents or delays their becoming solid waste? What follows are some suggestions which will inspire you to discover reuses of your own.

The greatest single source of popular home-economic tips is Heloise Cruse's famous nationwide column made up of work- and money-saving household hints sent in by readers all over North America. Many of these are good ecotips, and some of what follows can be traced to that source. If you cannot obtain Heloise's column, she has assembled her readers' suggestions into four paperback books, each under one dollar, and each an encyclopedia of delightfully pure Heloise:

Heloise's *Work and Money Savers* (1968)
Heloise's *All Around the House* (1967)
Heloise's *Kitchen Hints* (1965)
Heloise's *Housekeeping Hints* (1965)

These books are available by mail from:

Pocket Books, Inc.
1 West 39th Street
New York City 10018

Environmental groups publish lists of ecotips, many of which are reprinted in magazines. The U.S. Printing Office and the Department of Agriculture regularly issue home-economic bulletins. Personal experience, suggestions from family and friends, an eclectic collection of periodicals from the Depression and World War II period, and limited imagination have combined with the above sources to inform the following ideas.

Aluminum Foil

Foil sheets used for baking can be flattened and stored in a file-folder for reuse in baking; the same with freezing foil. When the foil is just about finished, crumple it into a wad and use it as a scouring pad.

Whenever aluminum foil is finally used-out, mash it

and toss it into the box with the aluminum cans and other scrap aluminum for the collection and recycling center.

Metal Cans

A clean metal can filled with hot water is a good baby-bottle warmer. Keep cooking grease sealed inside a plastic-lidded coffee can—these cans are perhaps the most reusable of all. You can line them with foil and bake cakes in them, or collect kitchen food scraps either for solid waste disposal, or, better, for composting. The plastic lids make these cans excellent food canisters. Steeping tea in such a sealed container is far more efficient than the regular teapot or bag-in-cup routine.

Coffee cans are the traditional Boy Scout oven, and can be adapted for stove-top use. For example, make a tiny stove-top oven for baking a single potato in 20 minutes. Can on burner, crumpled old foil on floor of can to act as a platform and to keep the potato from burning—put the potato on the platform, cover the can with another piece of foil, and turn the burner on to its lowest heat.

Always take a lidded coffee can on picnics for keeping the garbage off the landscape. On the way to the picnic, it might hold the potato salad. Mix paint in coffee cans, then seal them for short-term storage or disposal.

Nonreturnable Glass

Never throw out wide-mouth jars. Use them as decanters for dry foods or for breakfast cereals. Individually wrapped variety cereal packs are tremendously overpackaged and cost more than steak; just fill some jars with each favorite cereal and put the jars on the breakfast table. When you buy a large box of ecological detergent, decant some into jars for use in various parts of the house.

Use a funnel to refill nonreturnable pop bottles with whatever fruit or vegetable juice you want to drink. Cranberry and other juice jars are excellent refrigerator decanters for water or powdered beverage drinks.

Store lumps of cheese in a wide-mouth jar in the refrigerator; the cheese will keep fresh much longer and will not contribute or absorb food odors.

Baby-food jars can be used as baby tumblers; not as much milk will be spilled each time and the jars don't break easily.

These suggestions hardly make a dent in the range of possibilities; but the point is not so much to junk up the house with jars and cans, but to find places where efficient reuse makes them "disappear."

The Plastic Paradox

Because of what they do and what they are, plastics are truly miracle materials. Their properties generate so many uses that were the bags not considered trash, we would be *glad* to buy them.

Freeze everything in plastic bags, from extra ice cubes stored in the freezer to soup cubes to hamburger patties.

Don't make one salad at a time, but put different portions into plastic bags to keep in the refrigerator. If you line ice-cube trays with a piece of plastic, the ice won't stick.

If you're painting, line the roller pan with the large

pliofilm bag from the dry cleaner's and you won't have to clean the pan.

If you want to keep your hands clean when polishing shoes or furniture, use a small plastic bag as a mitten. Turn the bag inside out as you remove your hand and, presto, the dirty polishing cloth is neatly inside for storage and reuse or disposal.

Use a plastic bag with drainage holes poked into it for keeping kids' bath toys hanging from the faucet of the tub.

Make a see-through beanbag or doll for the kids. Use plastic bags for sorting spools of thread, costume jewelry, ribbon, gloves, stockings, handkerchiefs, and the like. Crack nuts in a plastic bag and the shell fragments won't go anywhere.

Strips of plastic are excellent for tying plants to stakes and won't cut their stems. Pliofilm is great for stuffing pillows. Wrap plastic film around the arms of a wire hanger for drip-drying garments without creases or rust stains.

Pliofilm is also excellent as an airtight wrapper for damp laundry until ironing; but be careful not to let small children near it. Don't, for instance, use it in place of a rubber sheet in baby's crib.

Plastic bags bought for special purposes, such as wrapping sandwiches or lining garbage cans should always be re-used at least once. Best of all is to not buy any at all, but use the ones at hand.

What about plastic bottles? Like film, plastic bottles can't be industrially recycled, and making a new one costs less than collecting and washing old ones for reuse. They can't be burned because some types which are dangerous to burn, such as PVC, contaminate the mix.

There are so many plastic-bottled products on the

market that until we drastically reduce their intake, we can only cut their outflow from our homes in a minor way. If a competing product comes in glass, buy it. Even if you can't reuse the glass jar or bottle, it can be crushed and recycled. Here are some reuse examples for the plastic bottles you still must buy.

Smaller PVC bottles, especially the soft shampoo or lotion bottles, are hardest to reuse efficiently. But if you make your own salad dressing, use a shampoo whose bottle is pretty enough to re-use as a dispenser. A larger bottle could be used for syrup.

Other types can be used for sprinkling water or vinegar (with a cork sprinkler from a hardware store), for filling irons or watering small plants. Recappable squeeze bottles (detergent bottles, cleanser bottles) can be used to decant usable volumes of denatured alcohol, linseed oil, gasoline-oil mix for two-cycle engines (lawn mowers, for example), or one-shot photographic developers. Always clearly relabel the bottle.

The third major class of plastic bottle is the translucent, stiffer, generally round, recappable type; ammonia and floor-wax bottles in the smaller sizes, bleach or bottled-water jugs in the larger. Although often PVC, bottled-water jugs are *excellent*, especially the square clear ones; they're clean when empty and can be immediately filled with juice or powdered milk or whatever. If you have a hobby such as photography, you may be able to reuse more plastic bottles than you can find.

Big plastic bottles can also be used to take drinking water on trips. Fill three-quarters full, put in the freezer a few days ahead, and as the ice melts you'll have cold water in the car. Fill it with hot water and it makes a long lasting hot water bottle to curl around. Fill it with rocks, tie a rope to the handle, and you've got an anchor for a small boat.

These are only a few possible re-uses; individual bottles often suggest their specific re-use by being transparent or not, shaped a certain way, or fitted with a special kind of handle, mouth, or reclosable cap or spout.

Re-using Paper

There is a major forest fire raging in each of our large cities, but unlike the disasters in our Western mountains, the forest is brought to the fire—the incinerator. Also unlike the mountain fires, this urban holocaust never goes out.

Aside from the long-term ecological necessity of conserving earth's forests, we must cut paper consumption for immediate health reasons. Mercury pollution is systemic, and now global; the toxic metal is found in the tissue of pelagic fish and mammals, those which spend their lives far from shore. Mercury causes brain damage, insanity, spontaneous abortion, and death. It is found in hazardous concentrations not only in the deep mid-ocean but also in fresh-water fish, mammals, and in ground birds all over the North American continent. Fishing has been prohibited in many areas; state Fish and Game Departments, rather than ban the hunting of contaminated pheasant and grouse, often prescribe that hunters eat none or only one of the poisoned birds every three months. San Franciscans are allotted no more than one striped bass a week from their bay, and pregnant women are urged to eat none, for mercury has an affinity for settling in the tissues of fetuses.

A substantial amount of this mercury comes from pulp mills and paper-processing plants, where it's used to retard fungus growth in the nutrient-rich vats of warm wood pulp.

While avoiding paper plates will not eliminate mercury pollution, all practices which in the aggregate reduce paper production and consumption will help. Enter the ecological citizen, whose re-use of as much paper as possible saves trees and helps cut mercury pollution.

Let's start with newsprint—optimally, it should all be recycled by companies such as Garden State Paper,* whose laudable efforts are currently saving 5 million trees a year. Until total newsprint recycling is effected, we can help by re-using it as much as possible.

Never use masking tape (it's paper) for protecting the glass when painting windowframes; cut a few strips of newsprint, wet them, and they'll stick to the glass perfectly. Use crumpled newsprint to shine glass, polish mirrors, chrome fixtures and trims; the ink works as a polish, much better than a paper towel. Newsprint is also excellent for polishing furniture—You can wash house or car windows with a solution of vinegar water and crumpled newsprint; always dry the glass with newsprint to take advantage of the ink's shining properties. Use newsprint for damp dustcloths or, in dampened shreds, to attract and hold dust when sweeping carpeted or hard floors.

After washing food containers, put a piece of crumpled

* See p. 121.

newsprint into the dried container, then seal it. The paper absorbs whatever moisture remains and the ink absorbs the lingering food smells.

If you use a fireplace, never throw out newsprint; it's not only kindling, but after being rolled tightly and tied, becomes the log. After all, it's made from wood.

Keep milk cartons full of sand in your car trunk or near your porch and driveway for sprinkling on ice. Don't use bulk rock salt for deicing; salt pollutes groundwater and kills streams. If your city or county usually salts streets or highways in winter, perhaps you or your group could encourage the use of sand or ashes instead. Salt also can cause great pain and damage to the paws of dogs and cats. Keep your automobile flares dry in milk cartons in your trunk; when the flares themselves are gone, the carton will burn brightly for about 15 minutes.

Because they're waterproof, milk cartons are good for storing wet food scraps for composting, or at least neater disposal. If you want crushed ice, freeze a milk carton filled with water then whack it against something hard until you can hear the crushed ice rattling.

Milk cartons, cut down, make excellent starting pots for flower and garden plants; the sides can easily be cut away when transplanting. If you must buy paper towels, bear in mind that you get one-third more footage with single, rather than double, ply. "Wet strength" towel doesn't break down quickly in water; add it to garbage, not sewage. White paper toweling, like white toilet paper, is best because the ink used on more expensive "decorator" rolls doesn't decompose; true, the whiteness itself is achieved with nondecomposable chemicals (otherwise the paper would be gray), but why add to the problem with extra dye?

The mailbox also generates a huge flow of paper into our lives. Presumably, you are sending most of your junk mail back to your benefactor, but if you keep some, use the blank backs for note sheets, shopping lists, or recipes. Gummed flaps of unosilicited envelopes are good stick-on labels. A proselytizing ecotip is to write personal letters on the back of environmental action handbills especially if the handbill itself is a plea for saving paper, solid waste, or forests.

It is sometimes suggested that particularly offensive junk mailings be declared at the Post Office as "pornographic" and "obscene" in order to have your name removed from the sender's mailing list. Pornographers who mail out material must purchase monthly lists of people wishing to be deleted from their mailings. This new restriction does not, however, cover irritating wasteful junk mail in general. Perhaps the recent regulations on sexually oriented junk mail could be broadened to include any type of junk mail found offensive by the recipient. Until then, sending it back, complaining about it, and re-using it seem to exhaust the possibilities.

Small children are a superb market for re-using paper and plastic containers. Toys and games can easily be put together from boxes and bottles and lids which are not only brightly colored and safe but also reinforce learning of important early concepts.

Thinking Is Child's Play, by Evelyn Sharp (Avon paperback, 1969), provides an explanation of early child learning as well as forty specific games, in developmental sequence. Such games and toys, aside from being educational and fun, provide unequaled training for your child in that they not only encourage creativity but also train him from the beginning to look at common things as having further value.

Re-using Fabric

Alvin Duskin, California clothes designer and manufacturer, suggests that in ten years the idea of a private wardrobe will be outmoded, replaced by clothes pools among friends just as more and more commuters form car pools; in each case, a tremendous saving to the environment. Mr. Duskin, in an interview in *Rags*, sees a big leveling off in the American apparel business when clothing is pooled for *use*, and suggests production may slow to a half or possibly even a fifth of today's. Clothes will be thrown away only when worn out—and with multiple wearers, they will *get* the chance to wear out. But even with lowered American clothing consumption, Duskin sees foreign markets providing a greater potential for clothes manufacturers than they now have in the closed national markets today. The main thing, however, is to lower consumption:

In the long run, the only way we are going to have peace is to lower the American standard of living. . . .
. . . What everybody really wants all over the world is not our politics and not our art and not our culture, what they want is our standard of living. . . . If I as a manufacturer am only concerned with keeping up the American standard of living, then I am a very selfish man.

If you can't share your clothes with anyone or if the idea appalls you, you can still make substantial resource savings. Select items basic enough to be worn out—how many *Nehru* jackets have been *worn* out instead of thrown out? The fewer garments you own, the better off you are. Fabric should be chosen for ecological reasons, although there are so many qualifications that clear choices seem hard. For example, although cotton is sponging up valuable groundwater in the Southwest, a wool suit requires between 225,000 and 250,000 gallons of water to make—about 20 times more than a cotton one. Think of all the water a girl can save too, if her wardrobe is mini instead of maxi!

Cotton has been the staple fabric of our civilization almost since its beginning; wool, our other basic natural fiber, only accounts for about 4 percent of the total market today and will fall to about half that by 2000. Cotton requires over half the total pesticides used in America and over 70 percent of the DDT. It also requires defoliating chemicals to strip leaves from the plants so they can be mechanically harvested.

In all, per capita fabric consumption is expected to shoot from the current 50 pounds a year to 64 pounds in 1980. By 2000, total fabric consumption will be triple today's level, but here cotton's share will fall below 44 percent of the total fabric we use. Synthetic fiber will comprise at least 54 percent of the market—today, it is less than half. Of this, about half is rayon, which is to say, wood. In spite of the fact that synthetics wear longer and require no pesticides for producing or mothproofing (some antimoth preparations are used without consulting the consumer and are sometimes as much as 100 percent DDT), man-made fibers require up to 400 times more water. Synthetics also save ironing—electricity—but, in balance, are they ecologically advantageous over natural fabrics? The answer is a resounding YES! The one consumption trend which bodes well for the future is the growing major preference for synthetics, and *especially* nylon.

Even rayon, which comes from the forest, is better than cotton. It takes a year for 3 acres of trees to produce a ton of rayon, but it takes 4 acres of cropland a year for a ton of cotton. Furthermore, a ton of rayon is actually 30 percent more cloth than a ton of cotton. Clearly, land is much better used for rayon; furthermore, although rayon is cellulose, it need not come directly from trees—there is all that paper needing to be recycled. Imagine not only your newspaper coming back to you as a shirt, but an increasing amount of burned-out cotton land going into soybean acreage to be rebuilt.

Nylon is oil, and is just slightly less used than rayon. The trend is to nylon. This is excellent—it frees the forest, and uses fossil fuel so efficiently that consumption is almost insignificant. Just think of all the shirts going out the exhaust pipe of your car. How many more blouses there could be if we all drove economy cars!

The water-consumption figure for synthetics, given earlier, is really a paper tiger because the water isn't actually consumed (as with cotton), but, rather, dirtied. Even so, this is "better" than pesticide runoff from cotton fields, but if a water recycling system were built into every synthetic fiber factory, increased consumption would require a minor amount of new water from the river into the closed, recycled system in which the same water is cleaned and re-used as our kidneys clean our blood for reuse. But even if the factories "merely" put the water back the way they found it, riverflow would be minimally inconvenienced. Either way, the politics seem more difficult than the technology. It is possible, at least in theory, to have fabric without soaking pesticide and defoliants into cropland.

If your wardrobe is not only mini, but nylon as well, it's not only better quality, but far more ecologically sane.

Although less expensive, cotton is an ecological luxury. We should not only cut consumption, but greatly increase recycling. Also reuse it as much as possible. Make old towels into wash and dish cloths, bath mittens, aprons; use for dusting, or in place of paper towels.

Shirts can be reused again and again. Keep replacing worn collars and cuffs with extras bought from notions departments. Use the tail of a shirt to mend a worn corner on a fitted sheet; use the old sleeves to protect good sleeves when gardening. Use iron-on patches to stretch wear of children's and work clothes. Put one on the ironing board cover as an iron rest. Make an ironing board cover from a contour sheet or from an old wool blanket—wool holds heat and steam much better than cotton. Use, use, use, until the cloth is worn lint-free for fine polishing.

Nylon consumption should be increased, but only at the expense of cotton, wool, and rayon. Once we have the nylon garment, however, reuse it—especially if the reuse displaces cotton. Unfortunately, it's difficult to reuse most nylon garments because the fabric doesn't absorb as does cotton, but the coarser nylon weaves (stockings, panty hose) provide many reuses. A nylon stocking is a superior shoe rag. The weave is also good for filtering enamel paint, cooked starch, and photographic chemicals. Tie a nylon stocking over the drain hose of your washing machine to trap out-flowing lint in the toe of the stocking, not in the sewer or septic tank.

Nylon stockings or panty hose can be rolled into loose, airy balls and used as quilt stuffing. The nylon, when crumpled, is as lightweight as plastic film, but warmer and softer. Use two old blankets for an even warmer shell. Nylon stocking quilts can not only absorb *all* the old nylons you can get, but will not need airing or washing nearly as often as a feather quilt.

Because of its slight abrasive quality, a nylon stocking can contain soap scraps and work as an efficient dish scrubber. Old clothes that can't be handed down can be torn into strips and braided and sewn into rag rugs.

As the last resort, you can take your old fabrics to a rag-redemption center or contribute them to a church or school recycling drive. Your shirts and sheets, worn out, mended, worn out again, fabric reused again and again, might then come back to you one more time as the paper money with which you buy new sheets and shirts.

Around the House

Vigilance for ecotips doesn't end when you leave the service rooms; consumption can be cut in every room. Appliance repair, for example, cuts material consumption, but in many cities repairmen are either difficult to find or charge so much that just replacing smaller appliances is often tempting. Apart from reading directions, filing sales slips and guarantees, and learning to make minor repairs yourself, a good rule is to replace a worn out appliance with the same make and if possible the same model, if the old unit lived a good life before its final collaps.e If you replace an appliance with a similar model, be sure to remove and save as many switches, handles, and knobs from the old one as you can—they'll be invaluable for repairing the replacement. Thus the useful lifetime of many products can be extended considerably. Keep an eye out for double value in everyday items. For instance, why get a lot of different colors of shoe polish when you can unscuff colored shoes with a matching wax crayon? Why buy a new pair of rubber gloves when a regular plastic Band-aid will repair leaks from the inside?

Naturally, your painting drop cloth is an old shower curtain which you keep stored spread out under the bed —even in storage, it works as a dust tarp.

Bathrooms generate a minor amount of solid waste, but even this can be cut by not using useless and even harmful products and by reusing the containers of those you to buy. Uses for small containers are storing toothpicks, buttons, needles and pins, small nails, screws, nuts and bolts, and electronic parts. Salvage an empty 8-ounce mayonnaise jar, pour in about an inch of rubbing alcohol, and store your safety razor, head down, in it. The alcohol keeps skin oils and acids from gumming the razor and each blade stays sharp longer.

Old shower curtains can be laid over your freshly planted garden to retain moisture and heat during germination. If you dry clothes outside, make a roof of a shower curtain over the line and leave the protected wash out overnight to take advantage of the brightening effect of morning dew. Strip off the tarp, let the sunlight dry out the dew, and you won't miss those potent phosphate detergents with fluorescent brighteners.

Other specifics not quite so tiny: don't leave *anything* on when not being used, from light bulbs to car engines to water faucets or garden hoses. Don't burn garbage and leaves, especially in the city where it's probably illegal anyway. Be sure that garbage is neatly in the can; a good stomping will often double the can's apparent capacity. Use a plastic garbage can to cut noise.

Christmas, fortunately, comes but once a year, but an ecological lifestyle should follow through. Include a gift for your favorite conservation group by buying a living (potted) pine tree and decorating it with homemade ornaments; the tree can go in the yard, and when it's too big to carry easily, plant it.

Avoid buying presents as much as possible—make your own. An excellent idea book is Mary Lou Stribling's *Art from Found Materials* (Crown Publishers, 1970).

If you have spent the summer gardening or gathering berries in the woods, make some jellies and jams, put a Santa decal on each jar, wrap them in the comic section, and send them away. If anyone sends you gift-wrapped gifts, of course save the paper and ribbon. If you practice photography, give pictures; if you do beadwork, give samples. If your friends don't appreciate your handicrafts, some friends.

When you buy toys, be sure to avoid the dangerous ones or the psychologically worthless or even destructive ones; these impose on child *and* parent. Be sure to give only toys which are educational and fun and don't have sharp edges, make loud noises, or encourage violence or overt competition. Check the supermarkets for inexpensive children's books and records. If ou buy anything electrical for a child, it should be battery powered, *never* powered by house current. In fact, with the electric power problems, it may be best to not give electrical presents to anyone, child or adult.

The Environmental Handbook (Ballantine Books, 1970) contains, aside from its wealth of information, the following remarkable summation:

If you told the suburbanite that the way his house was built, the elimination of food-producing land that it caused, his long-distance drive to work, his work in the military-industrial-governmental structure, his use of power gadgets, his wife's consumption of clothing, his family's consumption of prepackaged synthetic foods, the daily pouring of thousands of food calories into the "garbage" disposal under his kitchen sink, and the birth of his third child are making the world unlivable, he wouldn't believe you.

Get him to believe you.

Ecology Action urges what they call the "life-house" concept, namely opening up your ecological household to your neighbors under the guise of an informal party or coffee klatch. Share ecotips at these meetings, show how time and money can be saved by cutting consumption and waste, explain how vital resources can be spared even through minimal lifestyle accommodations. Your neighbors can probably offer many of their corner-cutters which they hadn't thought of as ecotips before.

After you've had a few such parties, suggest forming a consumer's club. Even two or three families can save a great deal by buying and using in concert. Why, for instance, should four neighbors own four power mowers when they could buy and use one together? Same with snow removers, garden tools, rug cleaners, and on and on. Why not share magazines as well as car rides to the supermarket? Think of the packaging saved if you buy cold cuts and cheese in block form—savings can run up to 50 percent. Trade old furniture—maybe a neighbor would like to refinish and use that old chair and would be willing to swap for a lamp you could make a new shade for.

Share skills within your neighborhood club as well as

objects. If you sew, perhaps you could do some mending for a neighbor who in turn helps out with babysitting or carpentry or appliance repair. A consumer club or service-sharing group, aside from saving money and material, is also an easy way for you to introduce your neighbors to the concept of trying to live more in balance with the environment. It isn't enough to simply tell them, because as the quote from *The Environmental Handbook* suggests, they won't really take it to heart: verbalization seldom can change behavior as effectively as examples of doing little things differently around the house.

Six: Building Ecological Systems

Disposing of Sewage Disposal

Macrocosm—the whole univerfe; fo called in diftinction to the *Microcofm,* i.e. the little world or body of man which is frequently fo called.

Microcosm—the body of man fo call'd by way of excellency, becaufe of the admirable variety and couriouf frame of itf feveral parts.

—*Compleat Universal Etymological English Dictionary,* 1736, N. Bailey, Second Edition

The brief philosophical essay above is quoted from the fifth dictionary printed in the English language, the first lexicographical attempt that was at all comprehensive. Although our language was only beginning to be recorded, we already had the concept of ourselves as the miniature epitome of the universe pretty well established, and it stayed with us. While deluded that we were Nature's only important subsystem, we destroyed the real ones by mixing them carelessly one into the other. Only by artificially mixing the systems of the planet are they polluted. Sewage is food for the land, but poison for water; the ancient misconception that waste is properly dumped into rivers and lakes must within the next few years finally be straightened out and the basic underlying misunderstanding of "sewage disposal" must be itself disposed of.

We *are* microcosmic; everything in nature is, even the atom whose structure superficially resembles that of a solar system. Just as the earth has a limited amount of circulatory media, the water and air cycles, we too have limited blood supply. The earth has methods for continually recycling its media, so has the body: the kidneys clean the blood of wastes—literally, they recycle it. Perhaps if we can mimic our microcycling we can dispose of macrosewage. Every factory, office, and apartment building, and each home, could have internal water recycling systems which remove the waste from a contained amount of water and send the cleaned water back again and again until it evaporates from cooking or perspiration and must be replaced from riverflow. A fully enclosed system of this type, either municipal or individual, seems the only way we will ever live on a natural planet again, unless dieback reduces us to less than a billion impoverished primitives. This type of sewage disposal would be twentieth-century; what we have instead is a mistake mainly equipped with Victorian and sometimes pre-Roman technology.

If you live in Memphis, Tennessee, your sewage technology is not even technology at all; Memphis dumps 60 million gallons of raw sewage each day into the Mississippi, the "colon of the Midwest"; but Memphis is not alone—25 percent of the towns in America dump raw, untreated excrement into their nearest stream.

In total figures, about 20 million Americans put their excrement directly into water as raw sewage. About 100 million of us, just about half, treat our sewage by some degree of "purification," and perhaps 70 million others have no sewage-plant affiliation but depend on septic tanks. In per capita figures, each of us contributes an estimated 200 gallons of liquid waste material a day, industrial as well as household. Barry Commoner tells us that our treatment of sewage is so inadequate that municipal sewage alone will pose a Biological Oxygen Demand by 1980 which will equal the total amount of dissolved oxygen carried by all of America's river systems. This means that not only will we be drastically short of water in ten years but that all the water there is will be deadly to animal life.

The septic tank is a Victorian invention which collects the waste material from a house (septic means infectious) and holds it as it decomposes and then releases the nonseptic remainder into groundwater. It is woefully unable to handle the type and volume of septic waste from modern homes. They are putrefaction vaults and accumulate a thick and disgusting sludge which must be removed every few years; but because the tank is underground, beneath lawn and patio, they are seldom dug up and emptied. When they become burdened with accumulated sludge, they stop working and the material they infuse into groundwater is still septic—still infectious. Vast regions in the Middle East, Turkey, and Afghanistan have been continuously deluged with human wastes by large populations for thousands of years, and in these areas the land itself is now septic and can produce disease in humans.

Although protozoa and bacteria reduce some of the

septic potential of modern suburban septic tanks, they are not 100 percent efficient even when new, and after a few years are dreadfully inefficient.

At best, sewage plants operate at three levels: primary, secondary, and tertiary treatment. Primary treatment is the same type of action that takes place in your toilet: the heavier solids simply settle to the bottom. The settled sludge is disposed of somehow and the remaining rich broth is dumped into the river. Secondary treatment filters the broth, removing some of the larger particles which didn't sink to the bottom. Most of the treatment plants in America are primary; this "technology" was practiced by the ancient Egyptians—and it didn't even work for them.

Congress recently defeated a proposal for allocating billions of dollars for secondary treatment. Although we are unwilling to spend those billions, the goal itself is insufficient. Secondary treatment is nineteenth-century and cannot cope with twentieth-century contaminants, which are not filterable.

Tertiary treatment involves "activation" as the third stage; the decomposition of sewage nutrients by microorganisms. Only a few plants are so sophisticated, but this is really no answer for the nonnutrient chemicals of industry and the home, or even the nutrient in today's sewage. For instance, the phosphorus in sewage may be absorbed by microorganisms that feed upon it, but their death will pose a high BOD as the water they are dumped into tries to absorb them. And, of course, those chemicals which have no place in a water system will pass right through—mercury, for instance.

Sewage-treatment plants cannot "dispose" of waste. (The notion of disposal is a mistake, since it presumes that the waste vanishes.) It is the death of water systems if they must consume the nutrients which land systems have evolved to enrich themselves. Furthermore, displacing this organic enrichment impoverishes the land system; its capacity for reproducing organic material (namely food) is drained.

Man has built as many structures—homes, factories, offices—since World War II as had been constructed in all of previous human history, and will build as many more in only twenty years. Each of these will generate sewage. Perhaps the 4 million who founded our country could dump into their rivers, but their 210 million descendants cannot now, and the next 100 million's worth of excrement will totally destroy the national river system.

The New York counties of Suffolk, Nassau, and Westchester are so densely riddled with septic tanks that the use of groundwater for municipal purposes is jeopardized, suggesting that the land itself must be growing septic. Septic tanks even in rural Wisconsin are turning lakes into green algael soup. How many of America's 43 million boats have any but the most obvious means of sewage disposal? The Great Lakes states were, on an individual basis, passing firm laws against boat dumping, but the Nixon administration recently reversed this "total retention" law in favor of primary treatment.

Even modernizing our current methods just to the extent that we lay out the pipes and connect all homes to presently existing disposal techniques is estimated to cost at least $20 billion; the figure for including partial tertiary treatment is put at $100 billion, which is to say a commitment the financial size of the Vietnamese War from 1967 to 1970, or eighteen months of total defense spending.

Americans per capita require each day about 2,000

gallons of water to carry away industrial and household wastes. Before the Industrial Revolution took effect in our country, we used only about a gallon of water a day; even in 1900, Americans each used only 50 gallons a day. Obviously, we cannot cut back to these levels, but we certainly can decrease our water polluting demand. The notion that we will be requiring (which is to say polluting) an amount of water equal to the total precipiattion in 2000 is not only logistically impossible, but ecologically disastrous.

Preserving aquatic environments and restoring them to previously balanced conditions requires an increased delivery of fresh water to the lakes and rivers. Paradoxically, one of the first things which should be done is to *decrease* riverflow by reducing the rapid runoff from pavement and wasteland. The water from pavement is flushed through storm sewers, which generally mix into municipal sewage whenever there is a moderate rainfall; this pollutes the entire amount by overloading the treatment centers with such an increased volume of water that the total gallon flow cannot be cleaned as well as normal sewage volume (which is hardly affected by cleaning treatment in the first place). Urban runoff can reduce local groundwater as much as 60 percent. Excess riverflow from land runoff destroys aquatic life by siltation: the bed of a river, lake, or harbor is an important ecosystem; when layered with mud, all life depending on its buried food chain must die. The silt carries not only pesticides but also synthetic fertilizers. Both types of man-made watersheds flood river systems in a destructive way, with polluted water, yet to cut riverflow from these sources in order to flush groundwater and improve the quality of the remaining surface water would be disastrous for industry, especially nuclear industry, dependent upon the present unnaturally high volume of river water. Irrigation would similarly suffer.

The other method of increasing fresh water in rivers and lakes is to withdraw and pollute less of its ourselves. Our individual human waste comprises less than one-tenth of one percent the liquid volume of sewage. The per capita half pound of organic waste we produce each day is small enough to be handled by land-based disposal methods, yet by diluting it into liquid sewage, we increase the volume nearly two thousand times. About the time the septic tank was invented, an Englishman devised an "earth closet" which covered excrement not with a flush of water, but with a sifting of a pound or so of soil, the microorganisms in which would decompose the waste by essentially composting it. If we removed waste from water in the home, and then combined it with a medium such as soil containing a high count of microorganisms, the resultant amount of dry organic refuse would be small enough for simple collection. If the biologically activated waste were taken to a recycling center, along with the rest of the day's separated solid waste, domestic sewage disposal would be incorporated with comprehensive waste recycling.

The Federal Water Quality Administration is helping finance a hopeful start toward land disposal of sewage for the city of Muskegon, Michigan. The technique, devised by Dr. John Shaeffer of the Center for Urban Studies at the University of Chicago, involves holding the city's sewage in lagoons while activating it, and then spraying it onto barren land. In theory, we could rebuild all the depleted land in America by cycling organic nutrient back into the soil ecosystems.

Until we institute ecologically sound sewage disposal, we can only try to cut the volume of our individual liquid waste. We can also stop using the toilet as a garbage disposal unit. Filtertips from cigarettes, disposable diapers, and cooking fats clog sewage pumps and pipes; they also rapidly accelerate the build-up of septic tank burden. Any paper with "wet strength" will not come apart easily in water; do not put it into sewage. Toilet paper volume can be reduced by using single-ply instead of double-ply.

If water was universally metered, its consumption would drop as people became aware of how much they were using—you pay for your water one way or the other.

Although you may not feel inclined to not flush every time, the amount of water in each flush can be reduced. If you have a tank toilet, put a brick or two on the floor of the tank to displace unnecessary water; or weight a milk carton and sink it right-side-up in a corner of the tank.

Bathwater is also sewage. Assuming each member of the average family bathes once a day, they could save up to 100 gallons daily by taking showers instead. Shower water can be reduced to half by taking a "Navy shower," that is, turning off the water while you lather and scrub (one also saves soap). If one is in a position to take advantage of it, group showering is the most ecologically sensible of all.

The most important thing we can do is become aware politically of the essential error in our established sewage disposal thinking, and act to divert the flow from the land to the water. Because so many manufacturing wastes are potent chemicals which cannot be absorbed by the water system at all, industrial sewage should be the first to be recycled for chemical reuse or land disposal—biological oxygen demand of industrial sewage is over three times that of municipal waste, and it is growing faster than population.

If we don't truly dispose of sewage, it truly will dispose of us.

Ecological Washday

Americans dump enough phosphorus from their yearly detergent to each pollute a private lake 9 feet deep and 660 feet across; our average two pounds of detergent phosphorus are enough to make this pond bloom green every growing season. Paul Swatek, in *The User's Guide to the Protection of the Environment*, reports that the critical nutrient level for phosphorus in fresh water seems to be about 10 micrograms a quart. A regular 45-gallon wash containing a cup of Tide will bring 1,400 gallons of water to critical nutrient level; presoaks such as Axion and Biz contain nearly twice as much phosphorus.[1]

Our washing machines are a major killer of waterways, contributing up to 50 percent of all pollution from the 213 million pounds of phosphates used annually. We are projected to pollute 50 percent more by 1980, yet already 80 percent of our waterways have difficulty or cannot support life.

Human excrement adds about 1.4 pounds of phosphorus per capita a year; per capita detergent phosphorus is more, up to 2 pounds yearly, and in spite of protestations from the Soap and Detergent Association, evidence

1. Swatek, *User's Guide*, p. 157.

indicates phosphorus as the key to eutrophication of all lakes, especially the Great Lakes and particularly Lake Erie.

Now that we know about phosphorus, the problem is to get it out. The Soap and Detergent Association's vice president and technical director, Charles G. Bueltman, feels that municipal sewage treatment plants should remove it. This is a natural enough industrial suggestion; taxpayers would then bear the costs of building local treatment plants far more sophisticated than any now in use. Even if such plants were built, what would each community do with all the phosphorus? Adding it to commercial fertilizer is the only answer; it's the best long term answer for all sewage, of course. Unfortunately, such effective sewage recycling seems far off and we could realize the benefits now by simply eliminating or drastically reducing phosphorus content in detergents. This is, in fact, the growing national opinion; and if you would like to express yourself, write to:

Charles G. Bueltman
Soap and Detergent Association
485 Madison Avenue
New York City

You might also write to the Association's three main members who make the majority of American detergents:

Colgate-Palmolive International, Inc.
300 Park Avenue
New York City

Lever Brothers Company
390 Park Avenue
New York City

Procter and Gamble
Package Soap and Detergents
688 White Plains Road
Scarsdale, New York

Write the president in each case, telling him that although you understand that they realize the environmental hazard of their high-phosphate products, and are researching substitutes, you cannot use their products until substitutes are found which do not themselves constitute another hazard.

Nitrilo triacetic acid, NTA, was offered by industry as a substitute for phosphorus, and over 100 million pounds are now used, but is shown to pose even greater problems. NTA absorbs more oxygen from water than does phosphate. NTA doesn't retard algael growth. Furthermore, Dr. Samuel Epstein of the Children's Cancer Research Foundation testified before a Senate subcommittee that NTA not only pulls dirt from clothes, but also lead, mercury, and copper from pipes. Once in water, bacterial action on NTA and its combination with other pollutants causes the formation of potential carcinogens and has caused birth defects in rodents. The detergent industry is being pressured by the government to gradually remove all NTA now in use. As no recalls or time limits are being set, it's up to consumers to avoid these substances while urging their immediate removal.

When you write the people suggested above, also plead that they improve arsenic removal in their manufacturing processes. According to Dr. Ernest E. Angino of the University of Kansas, detergent contains shocking amounts of arsenic which serves no purpose—it's just never removed. Wash water can contain up to 59,000 parts per billion arsenic (government safety level is 10 ppb), and although we don't drink wash water, it cannot be removed at the sewage plant and ends up in our drinking water and food chain. Furthermore, the poisoned wash water causes dermatitis, a skin irritation not uncommon among those whose hands are in detergent frequently. At 50 parts per million, arsenic inhibits healing of wounds. Arsenic residues also remain on the laundered clothing and can be absorbed through skin pores. The poison builds up in the body like DDT or mercury, and adds to our slow but inevitable degeneration.

Enzyme products are a spawn of Novo Industries of Copenhagen, Denmark's largest chemical concern, which discovered during the early 1960s how to produce large quantities of any specific enzyme. Novo, the world's largest enzyme maker, is building a $25 million factory in New York State, and feels that in spite of current controversy the market for their product will continue to soar. The enzyme business is a $100 million a year proposition, an increase of over 500 percent since 1960; detergent enzyme sales have gone from nothing a few years ago to over $25 million annually.

Enzymes are giant complex protein molecules which act as a catalyst to break up other molecules. One enzyme molecule can break up a half-million other molecules without itself being affected; it can go on to break up millions more. There are over 20,000 enzymes vital to bodily processes, and work is progressing toward synthesizing them for medical application. L-asparaginase is an enzyme which destroys leukemia cancer cells, but not healthy cells; other medical enzymes are being researched for sickle-cell anemia and the prevention of tooth decay. Enzymes are used in cheese, beer, and other food manufacture—there is even a spray-on enzyme which tenderizes (digests) meat. Enzymes may also be used in waste disposal—perhaps to break down plastics. They may also find a place in converting air pollution to less noxious substances. Enzymes may find a role in agriculture, building plant resistance to pesticide and frost. The Germans used them during the Second World War to convert sawdust to sugar and then into fat for margarine and other cooking purposes. Enzymes are vital to digestion, circulation, sensory transmission, and even reproduction. They are a vital part of nature, obviously, but since 1967, when detergent's Big Three put them on the shelf in the form of presoaks, they became something of a public bummer.

We all know their names: Gain, Biz, Tide XK, Punch, Axion, Ajax, Drive, En-Solve, Amaze, Bold, Fab—and the growing list of others. Phosphate's role in pollution was understood in 1967 when the enzymes were introduced, yet they are at the top of the high-phosphate list. How disingenuous of the industry to use environmental spokesmen like Arthur Godfrey and Eddie Albert to promote such harmful products. Further, in spite of $100 million worth of ads, enzymes don't remove all stains and many which are taken out are removed by conventional ingredients in the product. The FTC has forced labeling to reflect this.

Even more bothersome to the soap manufacturers is the health hazard question. An ominous ripple appeared in British research linking enzyme detergent dust with lung disorders among workers making the stuff; the housewife is possibly also endangered by dust when using enzyme detergents. The FTC began its own study to determine how enzyme products can cause allergies, skin irritations, and lung ailments and has proposed that health warnings be printed on the box, also. Further action on this is being held up by the Soap and Detergent

Association, who are lobbying for their own research data to be re-evaluated to determine if the uncompleted FTC study is even necessary.

On balance, consumers should give enzymes in nature a big round of applause, but a boycott of enzymes in detergent on the grounds that they were introduced in bad faith, aren't as good as they are cracked up to be, and may pose a hazard which the industry is being very unsportsmanlike about preventing. Besides, what could be happening in the environment as enzyme pollution builds up? Because enzyme molecules aren't affected themselves as they cause other molecules to break up, what effect can these biologically free agents produce? No one knows.

Phosphates themselves are on the way out, the only questions being how fast and what will they be replaced with.

Suffolk County, New York, has banned the sale of virtually all detergents as of March 1, 1971, not so much because of phosphate pollution, but because of septic-tank contamination from other chemicals in detergent which are not biodegradable. Charles G. Bueltman, of the Soap and Detergent Association, called the pioneering legislation "irresponsible and bad technically . . . attacking the pimple on a mountain," although the acne-like industry "will not take action against the law at this time but will wait and see what amendments are passed." [2] Mr. Bueltman, as noted earlier, believes the problem is one for the public to solve with sewer systems it doesn't have and cannot build for a decade, rather than one for industry to solve by removing all phosphates from detergents.

2. Reported in the *New York Times*, November 1, 1970.

The House Government Operations Committee has unanimously approved a report urging not only the immediate labeling of phosphate percentage on all detergent boxes but also the elimination of phosphates entirely by 1972. A copy of this report, "Phosphate in Detergents and Eutrophication of America's Water," is available from the Superintendent of Documents, U.S. Government Printing Office, Washington, D.C. 20402—it's well worth the 40 cents. The report urges seven other important steps, including the removal of all enzyme presoaks from the market.

There are lists of detergent brands which tell phosphate content—the above report supplies one. Another is available from the Federal Water Quality Administration, Department of the Interior, Washington, D.C. Lists appear regularly in newspapers or can be gotten from any environmental action group. There's no reason to reproduce a full list here, but the following brands have been compiled from several sources as having the lowest phosphate content.

For Hand Dishwashing and Cleaning Hard Surfaces

	percent phosphate
Trend	0.0
Sweetheart	0.0
Swan	0.0
Amway LOC	0.0
Dove	0.0
Fels	0.0
Ivory Liquid	0.0
Joy	0.0
Lux	0.0
Bestline LC	0.1
Bestline Ziff	0.1

Shaklee "H" 0.1
Fantastik 1.1
Pine Cleaner 1.1

Other brands in this category are generally under 13 percent except Spic & Span, which is 40 percent.

For Automatic Dishwasher

Amway Dishdrops 0.0
Shaklee "D" 0.1

Except for Soft Water Finish (17.9 percent), all others in this class are over 20 percent—some well-known brands are extremely high; such as All's 57 percent, Cascade's 68 percent, and Calgonite's 47 percent. On the whole, you have a much better selection if you wash dishes in the sink.

Light-Duty Laundry

Duz Soap 0.0
Ivory Snow 0.0
Ivory Flakes 0.0
Lux 0.0

Aside from the above soaps, Trend and Blue White are lowest, each with 5.9 percent. Others in this class are beneath 20 percent.

Presoaks

All presoaks are extremely high in phosphate content, generally well over 50 percent.

Bleaches, Softeners, Boosters

Addit 0.0
Arm & Hammer Washing Soda 0.0
Borateem 0.0
Beware of Amway Water Softener:
83.8 percent!

*Heavy-Duty Laundry**

Sears Roebuck 0.0
Signature (Montgomery Ward) 0.0
Shaklee "L" 0.1
Arm & Hammer Laundry Detergent . 0.0
Bio-D 0.0

Don't take biodegradable to mean phosphate and NTA absence, as biodegradability means only that no suds will form after twelve hours in water—an innovation forced on the industry after the Great Froth of the early 1960s. All the other popular brands are over 20 percent, most well over, except Wisk, which is 17.5 percent.

Until phosphate is eliminated from all heavy-duty laundry detergent, we should conscientiously use one of the 0.0's to make up for the excesses of others.

Whiter-than-White Versus
Greener-than-Green

Environmental groups are urging the soap-and-soda washing method for avoiding detergents entirely. Before you can use the method, however, you must first remove the detergent residue left in your laundry. Simply put the clothes through the wash cycle of your machine, adding only one-fourth cup of washing soda, no detergent. If you don't get the old residue out, it may yellow your laundry and make you think the soap-and-soda

* Note: Check to be sure that any low or no-phosphate detergent says on the label that it is also free of NTA.

method doesn't work. Once your clothes are detergent free, wash them from then on by adding one-third cup washing soda as machine fills, then put in the clothes, and add one and one-third cup Ivory, Lux, Duz, or other soap for an average 8-pound load. If your water is hard, add one-fourth cup washing soda or one-half cup vinegar to the first rinse to get rid of soap film.

The detergent industry opposes the soap-and-soda method for obvious reasons, but their official concern is that it will "result in significantly poorer cleaning levels, and a cutback in the nation's health, sanitation, and cleanliness standards." This concern seems particularly specious in view of their balking the proposed FTC health warning for their enzyme products. However, it is only in the white-sheet department that high-phosphates excel—they can zap a white sheet whiter (not necessarily cleaner). There was no health panic in the laundry before detergents came on the scene in the 1940s.

There is also a certain amount of doubt as to how clean "clean" really is. Just as artificial flavor and color is added to food to deceive our perception, optical brighteners are used in detergents to reflect ultraviolet light visibly—the cloth looks brighter, but it is because of the brightener, *not* necessarily because it is clean. Interestingly enough, in North America the brighteners make a bluish tint because apparently we feel this looks cleaner, but in South America brighteners add a reddish tint which presumably appeals to a different "view" of bright cleanliness.

Heloise has many suggestions for more efficient laundry. First of all, avoid a lot of unneeded products by putting together a basic cleaning kit. Never overload the machine, but never underload it, either. When you add your soap, measure it carefully. If everyone did this, instead of just pouring it in, detergent pollution could immediately be cut by one-third. You may not even need to add as much as the label suggests—remember, when the water feels slippery between your fingers, that's enough. Heloise's washing method calls for about half as much soap as usual, same with bleach. If you have a washload of colors, add a half cup of ammonia for brightening. With all the stuff in the tub, slosh it a bit, then let it stand for 10 minutes. No more than 10 minutes, however, as after that the washed-out dirt starts creeping back in again. After the soak, finish the wash cycle, then add one-quarter to one-half cup vinegar to the first hot rinse to remove soap film and further brighten. Try her method, with soap and soda, and see if you're not getting clothes just as clean.

Always remember there's still soap in an empty box; slosh it out with warm water. If you're troubled with "ring around the collar," mark the ring with plain white chalk and let it sit at least a few hours or, better, overnight. The chalk absorbs the oil and the dirt then washes right out. Try letting your sheets dry on the lawn for no-bleach brightening.

Try vinegar for fabric softener, especially for corduroy. Clothes that tend to get grimy are more easily cleaned if a bit of starch is added to the final rinse. The slight amount of starch, too little to be noticed by the wearer, isolates the cloth fiber from dirt—the starch itself absorbs most of the dirt and is very easily washed out, taking the dirt with it. Saves wear and washing.

If you want to buy a water conditioner to soften water loaded with hard minerals, realize that the water conditioner does not distill the water, but rather removes hard minerals by replacing them with sodium. As this may increase the salt content of the water, don't use it for watering plants or for drinking.

As for clothes dryers, gas is more efficient than electricity but, because of shortages, perhaps, should not be used *unless* your community generates electricity by burning natural gas, in which case it would be more efficient.

There are dozens and dozens of trick stain-removal methods. For voluminous advice along these lines, send for the following booklets from the U.S. Government Printing Office:

> "Removing Stains from Fabrics, Home Methods" (25 cents)
> "Home & Garden No. 68 on How to Prevent Mildew" (10 cents)

Or simply consult Heloise for many, many techniques which don't require special products.

All in all, you can get your clothes perfectly clean without using the potent laundry products recently introduced. Cleaner washing must from now on result in cleaner water.

The Body Ecologic

Our bodies are rich chemical environments supporting complex microbial ecosystems. Balanced microbiotic ecology is as important to our own health as balanced species of wildlife is to the over-all health of the earth's biotic film. In this sense, we are a physical microcosm, and, just as we've recently discovered what harm we do planetary ecosystems in our ignorance, we are only now growing aware of harm done our physical micro-ecosystems. We must be more skeptical of drug and cosmetic advertising which opens every crevice and peers into every cranny of our body, urging we buy their product to "disinfect" it.

A healthy underarm contains over 15 million bacteria to the square inch—billions are in every healthy mouth. The total number and balance of these microorganisms changes continually with our diet or level of stress, but the "bugs" are vital to our health.

The nonprescription drug and cosmetic industry was founded in the patent medicine era, and although they have sophisticated their image since the last century, the tactics remain the same: the pitch is all. One leading cosmetics firm spends almost 13 percent of its budget on advertising, but only 0.3 percent on research and development. Mouthwash is possibly the best example that the patent medicine era lives on. Just as skin is nourished by the blood, not by concoctions smeared on its surface, breath odor does not originate in a healthy, clean mouth and cannot be cured there. Even onion-breath comes from the lungs via the bloodstream, not from a film or coating of onion essence which can be gargled away; some people have metabolic bad breath—the chemistry of their system makes for smelly breath. Apart from keeping the mouth clean, the only alternative is to perfume the breath to mask its odor, or keep one's mouth closed. Microbiocides such as mouthwash and underarm spray are not selective; like DDT, they kill all that they find, good with bad. Antiperspirants work another way, by cutting off the sweat efficiency of the pores—this is like corking one's urinary tract: much better to keep yourself clean and use the antiperspirant only for major public appearances. Odor, however, means you are dirty, that dead microorganisms are decomposing on your skin. A load of mouthwash or a cloud of underarm or "feminine" deodorant will not cure the situation.

The Food and Drug Administration has for two years been reviewing drugs and has found 369 of them to be wanting; the FDA in November, 1970, issued a list of 369 ineffective or unduly hazardous drugs. Many are among the most advertised standard brands; many have been among the 200 most widely prescribed drugs and, in total, comprise 12 percent of the 3,000 drug products which have appeared between 1938 and 1962. The drug list can be obtained by writing the FDA in Washington, D.C.

Linus Pauling, Nobel-Prize-winning Stanford University professor known for his work in biology, medicine, and chemistry, has recently published *Vitamin C and the Common Cold* (W. H. Freeman, 1970), in which he claims that one gram (1,000 milligrams) of ascorbic acid (Vitamin C) daily will protect against colds and flu, and that 4 grams will suppress a cold you already have. Dr. Pauling suggests that pharmaceutical manufacturers, medical journals, and even some physicians have suppressed the cold preventative power of ascorbic acid, which is very inexpensive, in order to maintain sale of more profitable nostrums, which make up a $50-million-a-year industry. Dr. Pauling prescribes a daily intake of a half teaspoon of powdered ascorbic acid; at the first sign of cold or flu symptoms, the dose should be increased by a quarter-teaspoon every hour until symptoms subside, and a slightly higher daily dose maintained to prevent the symptoms from springing back within the next few days. In tablet form, the dose is built up to 1,000 to 4,000 milligrams. His conclusions are being challenged; although ascorbic acid is not toxic, it may produce a laxative effect if taken all at once. Some studies indicate that pregnant women who take overdoses of ascorbic acid can produce children who require more vitamin C than normal. Human beings are unique in that they cannot synthesize this vital chemical naturally, and must have a daily intake. The reader should, however, consult Dr. Pauling's book and reach his own conclusions.

Nasal drops and sprays are increasingly suspect. Research has shown that although some nasal decongestants immediately shrink swollen tissue, the nasal passages soon swell up more than before, leading to an increased dose the next time. Worse, the aerosol sprays, particularly used for asthma relief, contain fluroalkane gas, often called Freon, used to propel the product in mist form. There are reports of over fifty sudden heart failures while inhaling from aerosol bronchodilators—Freon is toxic to the heart and, because it is heavier than air, tends to settle in the lungs and then be taken into the heart via the blood. It can kill very quickly; asthma victims have been found dead still clutching their empty aerosol nebulizer. Children trying to "turn on" with aerosol spray have also been found dead. Aerosol cans are hazardous to dispose of, as it says on the label. How much fluroalkane do you inhale from room fresheners, cosmetics, deodorants, hair spray, and other such common sources?

In spite of products such as Cupid's Quiver, "the first gyna-cosmetic," a vaginal flavoring, it is difficult to comprehend the perverse nature of commercialized "hygiene." Perfumed toilet paper is a medical hazard—it can cause dermatitis—but who would have imagined that anyone would have taken it seriously in the first place?

Other products sell themselves by planting us with the

"symptoms" they will "relieve." Sominex suggests that if it "sometimes takes over 15 minutes to fall asleep" we should ingest their brand of the hallucinogen scopolamine. Scopolamine is often used in the preoperative shot in hospitals; it prepares the patient for surgery by bringing his consciousness "down" far enough so he will not leap screaming from the operating table as he is readied for the sodium pentathol and the scalpel. The effect is to dampen his awareness of impending danger. There have been cases of pseudo schizophrenia reported from overuse of sleep-inducing products, and scopolamine was indicated in each case. Even if you do not "trip out" on your sleep-inducing tablets, the drug could work to reduce your response to danger. Besides, it *always* takes me more than 15 minutes to go to sleep. Especially when I lay there thinking of all the drugs and nostrums I've been suckered into using during my deluded youth.

Weems L. Clevenger, an FDA district director said recently:

> . . . the contamination of cosmetics and topical drugs (those which are applied to a specific body area) with pathogenic (infectious) bacteria has reared its ugly head higher and higher in the past two years or so. . . . The industry involved is not taking adequate steps to assure itself and the public that its products are not contaminated with pathogenic bacteria.

The above was said in connection with a tested sample of 250 cosmetics, of which 61 were contaminated, including products by the leading names in the industry. Apart from potential infection, skin creams containing estrogen should be avoided because there is no medical evidence that estrogen rubbed on the skin does anything more beneficial than mud, but it may well be harmful to be exposed to this powerful hormone. Probably the best favor we can do for our skin is simply to keep it clean. If you wish to play games with your skin, at least use natural ingredients—many such products are now being introduced.

Besides the questionable purity and effectiveness of popular drugs and cosmetics, these multibillion-dollar industries contribute more than their share to solid waste: not only vastly more advertising than research or inspection, but elaborate multiple packaging combining glossy overwrapping with tiny bottles.

Common sense is often better than cosmetics or topical drugs; acne isn't caused by an absence of Clearasil; body odor doesn't result because your deodorant died; mouthwash does more harm than good—it does *no* good. Dyeing your hair will increase the odds that it will break or fall out. Why brush with sweetened detergent toothpaste when baking soda and water will not only clean teeth more effectively, but will also neutralize mouth acids which can promote tooth decay. A clean scalp is the best treatment for dandruff—wash hair more frequently and use less shampoo. If you honestly believe you need a genital deodorant, take a shower without further delay; don't risk dermatitis by spraying such delicate tissue with chemicals.

Many basic cosmetics can be made with natural ingredients from the kitchen, saving not only money, but packaging. For instance, soothing bath oil for dry, sensitive skin can be made by dissolving a small handful of baking soda and then sloshing three or four tablespoons of corn oil in a hot tub. Or, if you use hard water for rinsing hair or face, soften it with a teaspoon of vinegar per sinkful.

If beauty tips do the job of a commercial product,

why not save yourself the money and your environment the empty bottle by using them?

In the Garden

Gardening, man's first sign of civilization, his oldest art and science, is coming alive in the backyards of suburbs all over the country. The conventional suburban development is the greatest waste of land since the Romans salted Carthage. If you don't have a big enough yard, why not persuade the neighbors on either side to take down the last ten feet of fence and make a common garden through your three lots? If you share the land, share the labor and costs, too. A larger garden of this type will provide each with more produce than he could get separately.

The material in this chapter is hardly the last word, and sources will be given for more details, but if you don't garden, you can get an idea of what's involved and how to begin, and if you already garden, perhaps there'll be a few useful suggestions.

A fairly small garden, say 10 by 100 feet, can produce enough fresh vegetables to feed an average family during growing season; a garden twice as large will feed the family all year if the produce is properly stored and preserved. A booklet about preserving and freezing foods can be obtained by sending 35 cents to:

Miss Hattie Kilgore, Director
Research and Educational Department
Kerr Glass Manufacturing Corporation
Sand Sand Springs, Oklahoma 74063

An excellent cookbook which provides much information besides recipes is the *Home Garden Cookbook*, by Ken and Pat Kraft (Doubleday & Company, 1970).

Unless you plan to preserve, don't make the mistake of planting more than your family can eat during harvest. Radishes, for instance, come to harvest within a month and are good for one week. Plant a three-foot row for each radish eater, and plant the rows a week apart so as one is harvested, the other is ripening. Get expert recommendations as to local growing season from your nurseryman, garden supply store, or local garden club.

Snap beans should be planted in 5- to 10-foot rows, one row every two weeks; they'll bear great amounts of pods for short intervals. Spinach and peas need the cooler weather earlier in the season, and can't be staggered into summer. Other good vegetables for smaller gardens include tomatoes, lettuce, carrots, green onions, cucumbers (climbing), and sweet peppers. With more space you can include potatoes, melons, and corn. Stretch garden space by planting herbs or fern-type plants (such as carrots) in with flowers. Frilly lettuce also dresses up the flower garden, as does mustard. Beans, peas, cucumbers, and other climbing plants go vertically up poles, so they don't take much room. Tall plants, such as corn, can go right along the alley (unless they'd throw shade on the rest of the garden). Lay the garden out so shorter plants are in front of taller ones from the sun's point of view.

How much to plant is up to you; on the average, a 50-foot row of each of the following will yield:

> asparagus .... 13 pounds
> snap beans 12
> carrots 38
> sweet corn 22

cucumbers 55
lettuce 29
green peas 4
potatoes 67
spinach 13
tomatoes 79

A good gardener in a fair climate can triple these yields.

Increase yields by planting multiple crops during the growing season, but don't use the same space for the same vegetable. Rotate crops, bearing in mind that some plants require more sun than others, fruit-bearers especially. If you plant a few rows of a crop which has a long growing season, plant a quick crop between the rows of a slow crop; after harvesting the slow crop, plant a quickie in its place that can mature before the first frost.

Basic garden tools are a long-handled spade, rake, hoe, regular and soaking (perforated) hose, trowel, bucket, cord, and stakes. The "earth closet" noted earlier could even fertilize the family's garden as a modern version of Asian use of human manure in agriculture.

Before you begin working the soil, it should be just moist enough to compress into a lump that can be broken up between thumb and fingers. If it crumbles, it's too dry; if it doesn't break, it's too wet to work. Always work commercial fertilizer into the soil about six inches— don't leave it lying on the surface to burn plants, wash into sewage systems, and pollute nearby streams. The best fertilizer to use is compost. When planting seeds, be sure they come into intimate contact with soil moisture: wet the soil, press the seed gently into it, cover with about an inch of soil, press gently, and, if you wish, water lightly. Check the back of the packet if you're using purchased seeds. Use the perforated hose to soak each row about once a week; don't sprinkle each day, you only waste water and discourage root growth. If the ground's surface looks parched, dig a few inches under to see if the subsoil is damp; if it is, don't water.

If you want to build up your soil for a year or so before planting your first crop, start a compost pile, but check local zoning regulations to see if it's permitted. Many gardeners think a compost pile is a garbage heap and end up with reeking, putrefying mounds which give the science of composting a bad name at the zoning committee. Build your pile in a secluded corner of the yard where it can "cook" undisturbed and undisturbingly. Normally, a compost box, always above ground, is about 5 or 6 feet square and about as high; be sure to build the walls of the box so they ventilate—leave gaps between the planks or use chicken wire; the box should have a gate front so you can get at the cooked compost layers but dogs and children can't.

You can put almost anything organic into a compost pile as you build up the layers, but *never* put bones or meat scraps into the mix (they attract pests), and don't use obviously infected matter. Alternate each 6-inch layer of organic matter with a layer of soil; if the soil contains earthworms, so much the better. The organic matter should also be generally enriched with a touch of fertilizer, about a cup of ammonium sulfate, a half cup superphosphate, a tablespoon of epsom salt per bushel of organic matter is one recipe—or just use lawn fertilizer, but sparingly; the microbes don't need much, and the whole idea is to get away from synthetic fertilization. Wood ashes are also good, unless the seed packages say the plants are acid-loving. If you use a lot of leaves, they should be shredded and enriched with about 4 pounds of ammonium nitrate per 100 pounds to help the leaves decompose. Grass clippings, manure, sewage sludge, coffee grounds, and sawdust require no additional nitrogen to break down—in fact, they supply nitrogen.

The compost heap should be moist, but not sopping. The center of the top layer should be concave to help retain moisture. The compost is warm when it's cooking; when the center of the pile is cool, you know the compost is finished and ready for application. The time varies—many compost piles cook for years, being added to and taken from as older layers mature. Although it is more bulky than synthetic fertilizer, there is far less chance of damaging your plants by adding too much of it since it releases its nitrogen gradually. Don't use eucalyptus leaves or white pine or California incense cedar sawdust—these are poisonous to plants. Nor any sawdust that's acrid or sharp-smelling. Do use corn cobs, shredded paper and small pieces of cardboard, sewage treatment plant sludge and horse manure if you can get it, and egg shells. Naturally, it's best to have a mix of organic material in each layer.

The value of compost is that land nutrition is returned to the land and not put to poison waters. The technique is as old as agriculture, and compost is not only a fertilizer, but a soil builder. The compost should be worked into the soil before planting; after planting, continue to work your maturing compost between the rows. For more detailed information on this mircobial science, consult:

> *Compost Science Magazine*
> Compost Science
> 33 East Minor Street
> Emmaus, Pennsylvania 18049

Jerome Goldstein, who edits *Compost Science*, has

also written *Garbage as You Like It* (Rodale Books, 1969), which provides "a plan to stop pollution by using our nation's wastes." Same address.

Mulching is also important to good gardening; mulch can be leaves, grass cuttings, sawdust, or wood chips. Mulch provides some nutrient, but its main function is to cover and hold moisture in the soil and prevent wind and water erosion, like the layer of pine needles in the forest. Don't work mulch into the soil—it's supposed to be a layer over the soil. Pine needles make excellent mulch, especially in windy areas. Your parks department probably has its hands full of mulch they'd love to contribute to your garden. If you have evergreens, keep them mulched until they shed enough of their own needles. Mulch the garden just before winter and immediately after spring planting to help retain important early heat. Good mulching will cut watering tremendously, making your garden's produce a bigger bargain.

The question of insect pest control is controversial. Skilled gardeners can usually avoid synthetic pesticides entirely by keeping a balance of shade and sun, good watering, trees and shrubs to encourage bird life, and a variety of plants to discourage an abundance of any single insect species. The object, after all, is to create a *garden*, not a miniature monocrop. The garden should include rock gardens with small pools containing goldfish, minnows, and frogs, all of which eat insects and insect larvae. Your garden should also have predatory insects to help maintain control over pest insects. Ladybugs can be purchased by the gallon (75,000 in each gallon), and each bug can eat 40 to 50 aphids daily until the pest is gone, at which point the ladybug population drops. Order from:

Bio Control Company
Route 2, Box 2397
Auburn, California 95603

Get praying mantises from:

Eastern Biological Control Company
Route 5, Box 379
Jackson, New Jersey 08527

The July, 1970, *Organic Gardening and Farming* presents a list of other suppliers for other control insects. Seed catalogs often list plant varieties which have been bred to be immune to certain pests.

Many pest problems come from trying to grow exotics which cannot thrive in temperate climates; plan your vegetable and flower mix to include only those suited for your climate. Don't plant your garden in regular rows—your harvest will be by hand, anyway, and if the rows are crooked the insect has a more difficult time migrating from plant to plant. Some flowers are notorious for pests—roses, for instance, almost always end up with aphids. Mix flowers into your garden which contain natural pesticides; chrysanthemums, marigolds, and other asters contain pyrethrum. Put some of these flowers in with the tomatoes and strawberries. Tomatoes and asparagus will protect each other from root-attacking nematodes and asparagus beetle; in a similar way, green beans and potatoes defend each other. Garlic, chives, and onions repel aphids. Sage and mint protect broccoli, cabbage, cauliflower, Brussels sprouts; mint and basil discourage flies—keep a potted herb in your kitchen. *Organic Gardening and Farming* magazine is the best source of this type of information. Many companies specialize in insect-repelling herbs; write:

Greene Herb Gardens
Greene, Rhode Island, 02872

Snow-Line Farm
Route 1, Box 270
Yacaipa, California 92399

Avoid using herbicides; dig weeds out and if they have not gone to seed, use them as mulch or in compost. Don't use chemical weed killers on lawns—and keep children away from a neighbor's lawn if it has been so treated. Pregnant women should avoid herbicides, particularly 2,4,5-T which is still being used although there is strong evidence that it causes deformities in developing human fetuses. Mulching is a good way to keep weeds down between garden rows, and for crabgrass and other lawn weeds, water only infrequently, but soak when you do—grass has longer roots than most weeds, and will thrive, crowding out the shorter-rooted weeds which will not be able to absorb water held at deeper soil levels. Plant grass seed in the autumn, so the lawn will have a head-start on weeds; a fertile, healthy lawn will crowd out weeds, but the few which remain can be dug out by hand.

If you must use pesticides, use botanicals such as pyrethrin (allethrin is a synthetic version), ryania, sabadilla, rotenone, or nicotine sulfate. Avoid anything whose label reads *Danger* or *Warning* or *Caution* or *Poison*.

Research is active in the area of "clean" pesticides, and there should be many types on the home-gardening market soon; there is still a lot of DDT around, so don't use any of it. Also don't use parathion: it's related to nerve gas and just touching it can make you sick; the Agriculture Department is constantly receiving reports of parathion deaths. In order to maintain their fantastic per-acre yields, the Japanese use so much pesticide that beneficial insects have been all but eliminated; Japanese apple trees must now be pollinated by hand. America isn't all that far from such a disaster; but about 90 percent of the million types of insects are either beneficial or harmless. We seem to react to them irrationally, however, drenching parks and roadsides with overkill. The city of Berkeley was persuaded to forgo regular pesticide spraying in 1970, and hasn't been carried off by locusts yet; if your city or county sprays as a regular policy, find out if it's really necessary—chances are it isn't—and join in an effort to stop the spraying in favor of planting trees and shrubs to encourage birds. Some kinds of birds eat up to 6,000 insects a day, so a few bird houses and some bushes is probably all the pest control program you'll need.

Plant trees. According to an estimate made during the 1970 annual Congress of the American Horticultural Society, one tree would be enough to recycle the carbon dioxide produced by one man's breathing, but because of the vast CO_2 produced by automobiles, electrical generation, home heating, etc., a per capita share of the total CO_2 requires seventy-eight trees for recycling. We need many, many more trees throughout suburban America. For information about growing trees, contact:

American Horticultural Society
2401 Calvert Street N.W.
Washington, D.C. 20008

Poplars and willows are fast-growing and beautiful; a row of tall, thin poplars is better than a fence, and weeping willows can turn a plain yard into a mansion of bowers. Fertilize your trees by drilling 8-inch holes every few feet, starting a couple feet from the trunk and extending as far as the branches overhang. Fill the holes with compost, and then water, and leave them to close themselves. If your trees become blighted, cut away the diseased wood and burn it to destroy the infestation; never put it in the compost pile. Other than apples, don't go for fruit trees, they'll involve you with pesticides.

If you have no trees at all, and don't want to wait for them to grow from slips, buy nursery trees; your nurseryman can tell you how to transplant them, and what kinds are best for your area.

Keep a plastic wastebasket or large coffee can in the kitchen for compost material; save cooking grease for birds—don't put it down the drain to clog plumbing. Use newspapers or dry-cleaning plastic to cover planted rows as heat and moisture retainers; after the rows have sprouted, move the shields between the rows to retard weeds. Plastic bleach jugs, with tops cut off, are excellent for tomato hothouses; so are plastic bags.

Indoors, use plastic bags to cover houseplants when you go on short trips; the bag will retain about a week's worth of moisture. Stretch a plastic bag over a cut-down milk carton and attach it with a rubber band to make an excellent germinator for seedlings.

This is only an encouragement to gardening, not the last word. For that, contact the following:

Organic Gardening & Farming (magazine)
Rodale Press
Emmaus, Pennsylvania 18049

National Association of Gardeners
1000 Dilworth Road
Willow Run, Delaware

"Suburban and Farm Vegetable Gardens"
(Home and Garden Bulletin No. 9)
U.S. Government Printing Office
Washington, D.C.

Also, write your state agricultural service for soil and climate information appropriate to where you live.

Remember that for every organically grown fruit and vegetable you eat, that much less pesticide had to be added to the world. Apart from this over-all ecological satisfaction, the real reward for even the simplest garden is its first salad.

Seven: Defending Ecological Systems

Energy Ecotips and Kilowatt Capers

Just as fossil fuels power our car, they fuel most of the wattage powering our home, and we must lower kilowatts per month just as we try to increase miles per gallon in the car.

Electrical terminology can be confusing, but it is the wattage—or kilowattage—which determines power consumption. A kilowatt is 1,000 watts, a measured volume of electricity. You buy electricity by the kilowatt-hour, the number of 1,000-watt "cupfuls" you burn each hour. The trick, then, is to consume fewer kilowatts per hour of lifestyle.

One kilowatt-hour could be spent reading by a 100-watt bulb for ten hours. Or we can cool ourselves with a 16-inch fan for five hours, or listen to twenty records on a 100-watt stereo. Or iron clothes for one hour. A good rule of thumb indicated by the above uses is that it's most expensive to make heat, less expensive to make motion, and least expensive to make light with electricity.

In other words, if you read instead of iron, you conserve kilowatts by reading. When looking for power to cut down, don't overlook the 250-watt black-and-white television many of us leave playing to no audience. Read instead of watching television and you save well over half the electricity. You'll save over two-thirds if you read instead of watch color television, and, as an added advantage, books don't emit radiation.

Although no family is average, the following breakdown represents kilowatt-hours used per month for various appliances; the figures are themselves averaged from several sources. Find the appliances you use, and, if you wish, add them up:

	Kilowatt-hours per month
Air conditioner, room	80–115
Blanket	12
Broiler	8
Clock	2
Clothes dryer	83
Coffee maker	9
Deep-fat cooker	7
Dehumidifier	31
Dishwasher	30
Fan, attic	24
Fan, portable	11
Freezer	100
Fry pan	15
Garbage disposal	2
Heat pump	1135
Heater, portable	14
Humidifier	13

Iron, hand	12
Ironer, mangle	14
Light (five 100-watt bulbs, 10 hours a day)	150
Mixer, food	2
Radio	7
Radio-phonograph	10
Refrigerator	60
Refrigerator, frostless	100
Refrigerator-freezer, frostless	152
Roaster	17
Sewing machine	2
Shaver	1
Sunlamp	3
Television, color	42
Television, black-and-white	30
Toaster	4
Waffle iron	2
Washing machine, automatic	9
Washing machine, nonautomatic	6
Water heater	350
Water heater, quick reheat	401
Vacuum cleaner	4

If you have each appliance (except the heat pump, and, where different types are shown, the model that uses the least power), and if you use them according to the average, you consume over 1,000 kilowatt-hours monthly, which requires over one million British Thermal Units of fuel-derived heat. This is why we have an energy crisis. Industrial power use is similarly staggering. One example: although the recycling value of a ton of aluminum is only $200, that ton required 20,000 kilowatt-hours to produce. Another reason to conserve kilowatts is the drop in power supply at peak periods—the whole business day in New York City, for instance. When there isn't sufficient power, lights dim, motors strain, the television image shrinks, and fuses blow more frequently.

Reading, sewing, writing, and similar activities require a great deal of light in a concentrated place. Don't turn on all the lights in the room, get a 75-watt reflector flood from the hardware store and use it about four feet from your hands. These bulbs are more expensive, but they last longer and aim their light in one direction. At 75 watts, you're getting more light than from a 100-watt bulb in a conventional lamp. If you have no objection to its starkness, fluorescent light is more efficient than incandescent, and runs cooler by converting over 4 times as much electricity into light instead of incandescent heat. A fluorescent in the kitchen and laundry could reduce to a quarter the energy needed to light these rooms. It takes about 3 pounds of coal to generate 4 kilowatt-hours; thus, using more efficient light sources, cutting out unneeded ones, and turning out lights when no one will be present can cut 50 kilowatt-hours from lighting alone and save 36 pounds of coal.

Coal is mostly carbon; as this is combined with oxygen in combustion, twice as much oxygen is required for the resulting carbon dioxide if the combustion is complete. Incomplete combustion may spare the oxygen but results in smoke. Turning off lights wil not only be positive in view of the energy crisis but will help preserve the natural systems of this planet from the pollution of combusting air and land elements together.

Just as there is a good deal of calorie loss in the food chain conversions, the energy chain also loses with each conversion.

Coal into heat = fire and wasted matter (smoke)

Fire into steam = steam energy and wasted heat

Steam into mechanical = electricity and waste heat (friction)

There has been a great deal lost to heat at each stage (except the first, in which the loss was to incomplete combustion), and even as the electricity flows through the wires, it must overcome the resistance of the copper, and this loses energy to heat once more. Think of the loss between burning the coal in the basement furnace and burning it in the power utility. This is balanced in part by the fact that the coal, being burned all at one massive communal fire, can better have its wastes removed to reduce air pollution. If you heat your home and water with gas, you save the conversion losses, although you contribute to the end of all natural gas.

The only answer is to cut down. No more silly little motion-saving devices. Electric toothbrush, shoe polishers, can openers, pencil sharpeners. No more unattended air conditioning. No more drippy hot water taps, $8 to $10 lost each month.

Laundry: Wait until you have a full wash load (don't overload), and avoid ironing as much as possible. Buy drip-dry clothes, tablecloths, everything—use a half-cup vinegar in the final rinse and they'll dry wrinkle free. If you use a dryer, be sure clothes are first spin-dried in the washer; if you can't spin-dry, put a few dry bath towels in with the wrung-out wash to speed drying.

Kitchen: When you buy a new refrigerator, choose a single temperature model which you defrost yourself. Keep it defrosted and its coils clean; be sure the door gaskets make a good seal. Frosty, dirty, leaky refrigerators work harder. Choose a gas range, unless your electricity comes from a nearby dam and especially if it is generated by burning gas. If you have an electric range, avoid the self-cleaning feature (if it has one) because this uses 3 to 4.5 kilowatt-hours (and if it's a gas range it uses additional gas). The fewer frills on either the stove or refrigerator (like automatic ice-makers) the less energy they consume.

Heating and Cooling: If you are choosing a heating plant, consider that although oil and gas are in critical supply, they are about 75 percent efficient, whereas electricity is only 30 percent efficient for home heating. If your power comes from a dam, however, electricity is probably the best bet. No matter what type your furnace is, the following should help cut your consumption and expenses by about half.

Always keep your heating system clean—clogged filters and dirty radiators make furnaces very inefficient. Have your furnace checked each year, but keep track of its efficiency by the degree-day method. First find the mean temperature by adding the high and low and dividing in half. For example, a high of 60 and a low of 40 give a mean temperature of 50 degrees for the day. The degree-day index is always 65—subtract the mean from the index and 15 is the result, so in our example there are 15 degree-days. Add the degree-days during the month and divide them into the monthly fuel bill. If those degree-days start getting more costly, you should have your furnace checked.

Insulate your house, roof and walls, from the attic down and save up to 55 percent of the fuel otherwise required. Weatherstrip all doors and calk windows. Make sure the windows and doors close tightly; get storm doors and windows. Plastic dry-cleaning bags can be just as efficient as glass if stapled over window frames or screens. Such weather-tightness is equally important when trying to air condition in summer. The more outside air that leaks in, the more you must consume to maintain even temperatures.

Pull down blinds and close draperies at night to create dead air spaces at your windows. Shut off the register or radiator and close doors to bedrooms during the day so the thermostat won't include them in the heat it regulates. Same with laundry or other rooms not in use.

Always turn down the thermostat when you are away. Keep it at 65 at night, and try 68 during the day; 5 degrees less saves 15 percent because it's harder to maintain that extra heat—costs go up about 3 percent for every degree over 70. A fireplace robs the room of heat when the damper is open; blocking the fireplace is often a tighter seal than closing the damper.

If the basement is in frequent use, keep it heated; not much heat actually escapes; most rises through the house, especially if the basement door is left open.

If humidity is only 25 percent, comfortable temperature is about 78 degrees; if humidity is 50 percent, 68 degrees is comfortable, so use a humidifier. The same comfort principle works for air conditioning.

Air conditioning is generally more expensive than heating, so use it well. If you have window awnings, an attic fan, and shade trees, you may be able to survive most of the summer without air conditioning. Try a humidifier and a fan instead. Dry air is not only less comfortable at easy-to-maintain temperatures, but also bad for books, furniture, and lungs.

If you must use an electric blanket, put another blanket over it to retain heat.

Kilowatt-hour consumption should be printed on every major electric appliance so you can choose the lower wattage models. There should be a policy against leaving office buildings lighted all night or lighting an entire office when only one desk is being used.

Electric utilities are usually monopolies in the areas they serve. They should have little need for advertising, since their main problem is that they cannot supply the demand which already exists, but in fact they spend over seven and a half times more on advertising than on research. Perhaps there should be a moratorium on utility advertising, at least until the energy crisis is over; in long-range terms, perhaps there should be a ban until the industry devises nonpolluting methods for generating power. Electric rates should be revised to make it cost more to use more. As it is, kilowatt-hours get cheaper the more you use—a benefit mainly to industrial users. Call the power company in your area to find out how much each kilowatt-hour costs—it's a great incentive to save power.

Energy Ecotips and Infernal Combustion

In 1968 there were 100 million motor vehicles; cars were being turned out faster than babies were being born for many periods during the last decade. As these vehicles rushed over 1.1 trillion miles that year, they averaged less than 15 miles per gallon and converted 25 percent of America's total fuel, or an average of 670 gallons of gasoline each, to poisonous fumes.

If parked an equal distance from each other, there

would have been 26 of these poison-gas generators on every square mile of land in America.[1]

This form of transportation gets by far the most of our financing; the $75 billion Interstate Highway System will be, when finished, the greatest construction job in human history; not only far, far greater than the Great Wall of China, but sufficient to make six sidewalks to the moon.[2]

One of every four dollars spent is for automotive products and service. More than $660 million is spent in advertising. As British author J. B. Priestley remarked, in America and especially in our cities, "the cars have become the people," indeed, one car requires more oxygen than 1,000 people. Sprawling Los Angeles is one-third pavement—60 percent in the downtown area. In Manhattan, which is solid concrete, there are more miles of cars (were they to be put end to end) than there are miles of streets—no surprise to any New Yorker looking for a parking space.

This is the most wasteful method—it isn't really a system—of transportation conceivable. In terms of passengers carried, cars consume five times the fuel of buses and ten times more than trains. We are moving away from a transportation system in America; passenger railroad trackage is less than half what it was twenty years ago. Our transportation "system" is increasingly either jet or car, certainly not rapid intercity transit or urban mass transit.

Like power rates, which drop as consumption increases, the oil-depletion allowance encourages excessive fuel

1. *America's Lifelines*, Bureau of Public Roads, U.S. Department of Transportation, 1969.
2. *Ibid.*

use; it should be reduced if not entirely eliminated. Taxes from automotive products should help fund mass transit; after all, urban nondriver taxes help build state highways. If we took mass transit seriously, it could not only be extensive, clean, and safe, but free as well. Without cars, the downtown shopping area in your town could resemble a college campus instead of a parking lot. Always support mass transit bond issues as well as attempts to lower the number of surface vehicles downtown. One group in New York City working for realistic transportation is:

Transit Crisis Coalition
119 Fifth Avenue, Room 600
New York City

If you live in a large urban area, find out from any environmental group the whereabouts of a specialized local transit group and see what you can do to help. Only helicopters and jets waste more fuel per passenger mile than automobiles. Back to the bicycle and the shoe.

Lead is added to gasoline because it is a cheap way to increase octane. Until now, about 20 percent of our total lead use was in gasoline, and diffused into the environment.

Lead, like all heavy-metal pollutants, is deadly to all animal systems, and the approximately 300,000 tons of lead from gasoline in each recent year have accumulated in water and soil and will continue to concentrate in food chains. Leaded gas has raised our bodies' lead content 100 percent. Use unleaded gasoline, even if it does cost more. The City of Buffalo is moving toward a total ban on leaded gasolines; encourage your city fathers to take similar measures.

A substitute fuel for gasoline seems unlikely within

the near future if for no other reason than the monolithic inertia of industry. Methane gas is produced by heating chicken manure, and an English inventor has built a car which operates on it, but it seems unlikely to catch on for general use. Fuel cells, which produce electricity by chemistry, still seem to be a long way off. Liquid propane gas is much less polluting than gasoline, and is already used by over 250,000 vehicles in America, but there is some question about its safety. And propane, like all gas, is in short supply. The steam engine is still being pursued, and the gasoline turbine researched, although both cannot match the performance of conventional internal combustion. If we all drove battery-electric cars, nearly half again as much fuel would be burned by utilities to provide the recharging current, so this is no solution.

Make your next car a small one, a subcompact if used for suburban driving. These get by on gasoline with lower octane so you can avoid the lead problem. Insurance is cheaper, and the lighter weight makes for less inertia if you drive into a wall (but for a more dangerous collision with a heavy car). All power accessories work from the gas tank, so avoid costly extras. An automatic transmission is more accurate at shifting than most of us are, so unless you're bound for Le Mans, go automatic.

No matter what size car you drive, remember that the faster you drive, the faster you burn gasoline and wear tires; at 75 miles per hour you burn gasoline and wear out your tires twice as fast as at 50 miles per hour; although cars moving as slowly as 50 miles per hour are hazards on today's highways you can still keep an even 60 and save.

If your car averages 28 miles to the gallon, you're using less than half the fuel of the typical American car. If cars sold in this country were required by law to do at least 20 miles per gallon, air pollution and fuel consumption could be cut by one-third. Were an engine inspection slip required for driver's license renewal, the pollution and waste from untuned engines could be similarly slashed. Keep your car engine well tuned, the rings tight, and so on. And don't leave your car running when it isn't occupied.

Never let the gasoline attendant "top off" the amount of gas when he fills your tank. Gasoline hoses have a built-in valve to shut them off when the tank is full, but often the valve will be overridden to round off the sale. This extra gasoline usually just slops out as you drive.

Drive sensibly: don't tromp the gas pedal when the light changes; let up on the gas so your engine can wind down before you brake: start speeding for hills before you're on them. Avoid a lot of single-errand trips, especially in winter when the automatic choke burns more fuel until the engine warms up.

Make sure oil doesn't leak out of your car and into the sewer system, where it clogs the works. When you open a quart of oil, cover the unused portion with a one-pound coffee can lid for storage or, later, for disposal.

The other major automotive petroleum use is in synthetic rubber for tires; apart from urging tire recycling, there's not a lot you can do except try to get more mileage by favoring better tires and lighter cars. If you do a lot of highway driving, find the speed at which you get maximum mileage (it varies from car to car) and try holding to that.

Apart from these few possibilities, we're basically helpless to substantially reduce waste consumption as long as the single-car theory underlies our definition of a transportation "system." The main force for change will have to be political and legislative, and we may be able to get this change into action during the 1970s.

Protecting Ourselves from Urban Air

According to Michitaka Kaino, chief of Tokyo's Metropolitan Research Center, air pollution in the world's largest city will force its residents to wear gas masks by 1980; the air, slightly worse than New York City's, will be "about 10 times as thick and poisonous as at present and we will have total pollution."

Los Angeles and New York City are just behind Tokyo. In Los Angeles, schoolchildren are not permitted active recreation, such as baseball or jump-rope, when the ozone concentration exceeds .35 parts per million, which it frequently does. Doctors advise 10,000 Los Angeleans to leave the city each year as the emphysema death rate doubles every four years. Smog causes heart attacks which result in freeway deaths. Clear mornings turn into brown soup through which airplanes land by instruments, through air that puts a corroding greasy film on engines and other metal parts. Doctors fear that by the time statistical data can be accumulated to prove the effect on lungs, it will be too late. Ecologist Kenneth E. F. Watt warns: "The incredible thing is that nearly all scientific and medical evidence necessary to predict the end of Los Angeles is right here in the University library.[3]

3. Roger Rapoport, "Los Angeles Has a Cough," *Esquire*, July, 1970.

When Apollo 10's astronauts reported sighting the L.A. smog blanket from outer space, Governor Reagan quipped that it was only "a smoke signal we are sending up for their safe return." Roger Rapoport writes that the "smoke signal" covers 97 percent of the populated areas of California; eye irritation afflicts 70 percent of all Californians; and areas of plant damage include 80 percent of the state.[4] Further, the smog is leaking through mountain passes and spreading into southwestern Colorado by direct observation from aircraft. Because L.A. voted down mass transit in favor of more freeways, the million extra cars to be added may push the aerial wasteland across the Continental Divide by 1980.

Los Angeles was the site of smog discovery in 1942 by Dr. Arie J. Haagen-Smit, who defined the pollution and linked it with automobile exhaust. But *nothing* has been done to reduce it. In fact, a disaster of major proportions is predicted for California cities within five years. The new exhaust control devices for cars simply don't work; according to California's Air Resources Board, they wear out at 8,000 miles and can actually produce increased smog thereafter.

The National Air Pollution Control Administration recently tested 700 rental cars made by General Motors, Ford, Chrysler, American Motors, and Volkswagen to see how exhaust control devices worked under actual driving conditions. The 1968 and 1969 models had been driven an average of 10,000 miles each, and about one car in three failed to meet federal standards for hydrocarbon and carbon dioxide emission, although the cars could presumably meet these standards when they were new.[5]

4. *Ibid.*
5. Reported in the New York *Post*, April 1, 1970.

Because rental cars are regularly serviced and checked, and "family" cars often are not, the odds may be 50–50 that your car, if a year old, no longer meets antipollution standards.

The Muskie Bill requires that cars made in 1975 conform to federal antipollution standards 90 percent more strict than the standards of 1970. Assuming no extension is granted the automakers, there will nonetheless be well over 100 million used cars in 1975 which will be immune to the new law, and whose exhaust control devices may not be working or simply nonexistent. Furthermore, if 1975 control devices degenerate in actual use, as current devices do, there will be little or no gain in clean air. The air may actually be *far* worse in ten years than it is now, in spite of current awareness and newly passed laws, if we cannot reduce the number of cars. There is one car for every two Americans, and it is poisoning them.

Furthermore, because control devices increase the amount of air used, they can increase nitrogen oxides as much as 50 percent while they temporarily reduce hydrocarbons. Dr. Haagen-Smit has suggested that these oxides can interfere with certain proteins which carry genetic information. Nitrous oxides also form nitric acids which eat lacy lung tissues, as do the acids from sulphur dioxide. Nonetheless we are better off if we do use control devices; properly maintained, they will at least cut into some of the 90 million tons of pollution from cars each year. Each of the three major carmakers has emission-control kits for cars made before 1966 which sell for about $10 and an hour's installation. Perhaps there will also be a breakthrough in control devices. A Danish invention which costs the equivalent of $8 reputedly cuts fumes by half and can be fitted in seven minutes. The unit is scheduled for production in Denmark during 1971.[6]

Although there is still debate as to the extent of air pollution's effect on increased mortality, a recent two-and-a-half-year study concluded that even a slight rise in pollution levels which may pass unnoticed can increase deaths by several hundred in a city such as New York. Children are especially vulnerable; growing up in bad air can retard growth and development and leave the child with permanent lung damage.

By far the most urban carbon monoxide comes from cars—in New York City, more than 5 million tons a year; in Los Angeles, 4.99 million tons annually. Carbon monoxide displaces oxygen in the blood, thus overworking the heart and starving and killing brain cells. It's menacing to everyone, but particularly to drivers. Slow-moving traffic is the worst place to be in terms of carbon monoxide concentrations, and the pedestrian, in a place like New York, is exposed to 30 parts per million CO, three times the federal maximum and fully 25 percent as much CO as if he were constantly chain smoking. He is also receiving lead in concentrations proven to reduce life span by one-fifth, and to cause sterility and birth abnormalities in test animals.

In spite of the Ethyl Corporation's ad campaign, which claims unleaded gas produces more smog than their lead-additive products, it looks as if lead will be out of all gasoline at least by 1975. The furor for cleaner gasoline has already produced one alleged mass-deception campaign by Chevron, whose F310 ("the most long-awaited gasoline development in history") is, according to the FTC, not new and doesn't work. We will have to be

6. Reported in the *New York Times*, November 22, 1970.

wary of what the lead is replaced with; as with phosphate replaced by NTA, the new may be no better than the old. Most nonlead high-octane gasolines accomplish their purpose with increased benzene derivatives (aromatic hydrocarbons) which could increase eye irritation. Automobiles already generate about 63 percent of the hydrocarbons polluting our air; a slight increase might make it harder for control devices to cut down the total hydrocarbon output. At any rate, the future for conventional control devices is bleak; not only is more nitrogen oxide created by trying to lower amounts of carbon monoxide, but the total number of new cars in ten years will result in annual rises of carbon monoxide over today's level. It takes ten trees one day to produce the oxygen required to burn one gallon of gasoline: we have fewer trees each year than the last, and control devices require more oxygen than regular combustion to produce temporary benefits at best. The mathematics are against survival and will probably remain so as long as internal combustion—"controlled" or not—continues to transport America.

Those of us living in areas overwhelmed by air pollution can join the bicycle movement—although biking through most major cities will continue to be somewhat suicidal until public pressure can result in such innovations as the bike lanes that have been common throughout Europe for decades.

Although cars are responsible for urban carbon monoxide, they do not contribute the significant hazard of sulphur dioxide; SO_2, perhaps more harmful than CO, is mainly the result of coal and oil burning, chiefly by electrical utilities and residential furnaces. Many people have purchased the portable "air purifiers" recently available on the market. Some of the units, about the size of a television set, have been criticized by the FDA for actually increasing the ozone content in rooms. Ozone, a rare, triple-atom form of oxygen, can decrease respiratory efficiency and cause eye irritation. If you consider buying a purifier, be sure it doesn't use ozone as its active ingredient.

To combat air pollution in the city, be sure to take a daily dose of vitamins A and E, which protect the lungs from being seared by nitrous oxides and ozone; they also help lung tissue in transmitting oxygen. Also, lose weight —the more you weigh, the more oxygen you need and the harder you must pant to get it. You're also consuming more food and clothing.

Raw fruits such as oranges, apples, lemons, peaches, and apricots are said to assist the body in flushing drug and chemical poisons, as do vegetables such as asparagus, raw carrots, raw celery, cauliflower, mustard greens, watercress, and horseradish. Poison-eradicating herbs include fennel, horehound, juniper berries, rue sarsaparilla, marjoram, and alfalfa tea. *How to Live in Our Polluted World*, by May Bethel, suggests the above and a great many other organic food and drug suggestions for consideration by even those who don't care to go entirely organic.

You may find yourself using eyewashes more frequently the longer you live in a big city, and perhaps even using oxygen-breathing devices on bad days. The oxygen breather is especially usable by New Yorkers wading through carbon monoxide; keep one at home or at the office to recharge your brain with oxygen after the stultifying walk to or from work. Masks are also available for children and adults and sell for $20. For more details write:

Survival Associates
333 East 55th Street
New York City 10022

If you live in an urban area and have respiratory problems already, you will probably need a bronchodilator, or even a pressure device to assist breathing before much longer. Be sure to avoid aerosol-types propelled by Freon.

Pollution varies in intensity during the day, being highest during business hours. During the year, it is higher in the Northeast during winter and highest in California in summer. Keep in touch with your local air-pollution control board—every big-city phone book should have a listing—and whenever ozone exceeds .35 ppm or conditions are described as "unsatisfactory" (most of the time in New York, Chicago, and Los Angeles), act accordingly by staying indoors, if you can, with the air conditioner on and going out only at night. Air conditioning itself doesn't remove pollutants, but cool air minimizes their impact and the filter removes some of the particulates.

A good general rule, and a vital one during a pollution alert, is to avoid all irritants such as smoke, dust, fumes, and spray from aerosol cans. Even if you won't stop smoking entirely, stop during a pollution alert; if you're in a traffic jam, get out as soon as possible even if it means taking a longer route. If you're walking, try to avoid clogged streets and when you can't, walk beside the building, not the curb, and *don't rush*—it's important to avoid stress and heavy breathing when trapped on a fume-filled street.

New York has initiated a citizens' smokewatcher program, so far including only forty members of Citizens for Clean Air. Although pollution inspectors are in short supply everywhere, volunteers are usually discouraged from filing violation reports because they lack the knowledge to include specific information required to make the charges against the polluter stand up in court. The smokewatcher's course in New York trains citizen volunteers by the same methods used for inspectors and pollution officials. Volunteers learn to match the smoke's color to a Ringelmann chart of deepening gray shades; the deeper the shade, the more severe the violation. Citizen smokewatchers, carrying the cards with them throughout the day, are able to file complaints correctly and can appear in court as witnesses. An increase in trained citizens would put real teeth in the new pollution regulations being passed by so many cities. A good project for your environment group would be to start a smokewatcher's group.

Even without the Ringelmann grays, report any and all smoke emissions which seem unusually dark and thick.

Other ways of protecting your lungs include trying to make sure air-conditioning ducts installed at home or in the office are not lined with asbestos or fiberglas—new techniques which save money for manufacturers but cost users a great deal in terms of hazards, including lung cancer from inhalation of asbestos and glass particles.

Another incentive for lung protection proposed by New York City's Environmental Protection Agency would allow a citizen providing evidence against an air polluter to collect up to half the eventual fine. This bounty system, a main feature of the 1899 Refuse Act for water pollution, should be adopted in every urban area.

Regarding air pollution, individual action will have to

be defensive, but group action can be aggressive: join with others in bringing suit against auto manufacturers for any damage their products' exhaust may have done to health or property during the period the carmakers allegedly conspired to suppress development of emission control devices. A federal court has recently ruled that triple-damage antitrust suits may indeed be brought against the Detroit Three, although a major case would probably be best brought by a municipality. Still, the action of your group may result in moving your city to sue on behalf of all its citizens.

Use your group—or even just the nearest bulletin board—to spread the word on the latest industrial polluter to boycott: Why continue, for example, to buy Eveready batteries when Union Carbide refuses to meet pollution standards already reached by neighboring Ohio factories? Each edition of the newspaper brings new stories and new names of violators of the environment, and if we diligently clip the articles and post them in stores, we could exercise our simplest, most effective tactic: nonpurchase.

Join the campaign in your community. If you live in New York, contact

> Citizens for Clean Air
> 502 Park Avenue, Room 416
> New York City 10022

and be sure to ask about their smokewatcher's program. If you live outside New York, contact them for advice on getting your own group started.

The truly ominous prospect is global air pollution. Already, the foul German, French, and British winds plague Sweden. America's breath is fouling the entire planet. Tests of incinerator stack gases in St. Louis have revealed extraordinarily high mercury levels, believed to result from the burning of paper (mercury is used in paper manufacture). Dr. Bruce McDuffie, who found the mercury in tuna and swordfish, believes that airborne mercury from oil and coal burning might be a greater danger than mercury discharged into water; he calculated that up to 20,000 tons of mercury are being vented into the air each year from fuel consumption alone.[7]

Air pollution is not limited to the rich, developed areas of the world, however. All of the nonindustrial, hungry nations struggling to industrialize haven't time or money to spend delaying their development until it will be nonpolluting. Similarly, many underdeveloped nations cannot afford to use any but the cheapest pesticide, which is DDT. Industrialized sections of India have pollution as advanced as any in rich nations. No one knows the potential for world pollution posed by the millions of people in the Soviet Union and China. The United Nations will have a world conference in 1972 to discuss the global pollution problem, but it can hardly be expected that pollution will be slowed very much for a long, long time thereafter.

It has been estimated that should all pollution stop tomorrow, it would nonetheless take ten years before the winds of the world would again be clean. We at least *can* afford to clean up and know how to do so, yet we continue to generate half the world's poisoned air. How will we convince the poorer nations to develop in a clean, but slow and expensive, way? If they do as we have, we will all suffocate in the international smog.

7. Reported in the *New York Times*, February 16, 1971.

Urban Defense Against Poisoned Ears

"What of the heart of the City—is it like midtown Manhattan where twenty percent of the population was found to be indistinguishable from the patients in mental hospitals?" Ian McHarg, citing Leo Srole, et al., *Mental Health in the Metropolis: The Midtown Manhattan Study* (New York: McGraw-Hill, 1962).[8]

Man didn't evolve in a noisy world. For most of mankind's time on earth the loudest daily sound might be birdsong, thunder, frightening us into religion, and from time to time the sudden predatory screech (which technique we adopted for human warfare). Loud and, especially, sudden, loud noise always meant danger. Startling noise has always been the signal for fight or flight. With the speed of nerve currents, the sound triggers the power glands, adrenals, to release epinephrine, a powerful stimulant which brings senses and muscles to an extraordinary level of alertness and strength.

This natural alarm response system is perhaps why we evolved the sense of hearing at all. Noise drives all creatures as a powerful stimulant which can of itself cause death. But urban surroundings are so polluted with extraneous noise that our systems are often in constant stress, the adrenals swollen larger than normal by continuous response to false alarms.

8. Ian McHarg, *The Environmental Crisis*, Harold W. Helfrich, Jr., ed. (New Haven: Yale, 1970), p. 17.

Urban living as such is not so stressful; studies in hungry nations note no increase in psychic stress among displaced villagers moving into crowded cities and exposed to urban influences for the first time. Crowded cities have existed throughout history without necessarily signaling the decline of the empire. The modern city, especially the American megalopolis, differs in one important respect from huge human ghettos in the hungry nations and from the cities of history—noise.

In *Moment in the Sun*, the authors note a 1964 survey by the Twentieth Century Fund comparing America in 1850 and 1950. In 1850, only 15 percent of the people lived in cities; today, more than 70 percent do. This exodus from the land raised industrial production and urban noise 35 times above the 1850 level.[9] Noise is increasing at a faster rate now; it is 8 times noisier today than in 1940, just before production was suddenly quadrupled by World War II. If the trend continues, 1980 will be twice as loud as today.

Noise is measured by decibel, or *db*, in a logarithmic scale; the scheme is complex, but the apparent volume doubles with every additional 10 *db*. The scale starts at 0, or the absence of sound, and records the gentle rustle of leaves as 10 *db*; a whisper at 20 *db*; a quiet room in a residential area at night is about 40 *db*; conversation is normally in the 60s, heavy traffic is around 90 *db*, a food blender and a subway, 70 to 100 *db*, and a jet at 200 feet registers 150 *db*. Hearing begins to erode in the 80 to 90 decibel range, noise becomes painful around 120 *db*, and can kill at 180 decibels. Noise is energy; the cochlear

9. Robert Rienow and Leona Train Rienow, *Moment in the Sun* (New York: Ballantine Books, 1967), p. 189.

cells translate it to nerve impulses, but high levels of sonic energy are converted to heat from vibration within the body. Noises at 100 *db* can generally be tolerated for 20 minutes before panic begins.

It is believed, falsely, that one can adapt to noise. It was suggested that "once we got used to it" the sonic boom would disturb us very little. Suggestions have been made for "masking" nearby airport noise by filling the home with low-level sound, such as from an air conditioner. But we merely learn to *tolerate* increased noise —we cannot adapt unless we become through genetic change increasingly deaf. The urban noise level has been increasing by 1 *db* per year since 1940, and the only defense our body has is to "turn down" the volume by destroying cochlear cells in the inner ear: hardly an adaptation.

Dr. David M. Lipscomb subjected guinea pigs to a total of 88 hours' exposure to noise at 120 decibels, approximating a series of discotheque experiences. Photomicrographs of the tortured guinea pig's ear showed cochlear cells to have "shriveled up like peas"—its only defense was to destroy its own hearing apparatus.[10] Similarly, three out of five American men have permanent hearing loss.

On June 13, 1968, the head of the Public Health Service, Surgeon General William H. Stewart, said that ulcers, cardiovascular problems, psychoses, and neuroses are shown to be produced by noise, and that up to 16 million Americans work in noisy conditions.[11] Later, he revealed that "it has been demonstrated that noise can

10. Reported in the *New York Times*, August 25, 1968.
11. Reported in the New York *Post*, June 14, 1968.

cause physiological changes. These include cardiovascular, glandular, and respiratory problems reflective of a generalized stress reaction." [12]

Dr. Joseph Buckley has subjected about 5,000 rats to a "stress vault" of his design.[13] The vault, about the size of an office safe, is shaken and jostled 140 times a minute to simulate conditions in a subway car; the jiggled rats are also subjected to bright flashes of light, loud sudden noises—such as clanging bells—punctuated with the sound of jets taking off. The rats soon develop high blood pressure, and it seems to be permanent; after a week of exposure they become irritable and dangerous to handle. The New York subway is very shaky, staccato, and loud—up to 110 *db*—and the irritability of its passengers is well known.

Dr. Samuel Rosen, of New York, one of America's most distinguished hearing specialists and ear surgeons, explains that in addition to psychic shock, noise makes blood vessels constrict, skin pale, pupils dilate, eyes close, the heartbeat increases greatly, there is wincing, suspension of breath, muscles are tensed, and the esophagus, stomach, and intestines are gripped by spasms. These reactions last up to five times longer than the noise itself.[14] Constriction of blood vessels is usually permanent, which increases blood pressure and contributes to death from heart disease.

Although men who work near jet engines wear ear protectors, they are frequently plagued with diarrhea, nausea, and pneumothorax (gas or air in the bag containing the lungs). Noise is also associated with higher-than-normal cholesterol levels in blood, which increases

12. *Newsweek*, January 26, 1970.
13. Reported in the *New York Times*, February 7, 1970.
14. Reported in the *National Enquirer*, January 3, 1971.

the hazard when coupled with the constrictive effects.

A report recently commissioned by the Koss Electronics Corporation recommends the household noise level be limited to 65 *db* to counter the "tired mother syndrome." Dishwashers, blenders, garbage disposals, knife sharpeners, and other kitchen appliances all produce noise over 70 *db*. Responses include irritability, depression, fatigue, and tension. "Tired mother syndrome," according to Dr. Jack Westman, who helped write the report for Koss, "is comparable to a soldier's combat fatigue." [15] At night noise penetrates sleep; although it may not awaken one, it disturbs dream cycles considered vital to emotional health.

Noise shrinks lymph tissue as well as blood vessels, and has also been causatively associated with hypertension, hallucinations, stomach ulcers, allergies, loss of equilibrium, impaired vision, as well as heart disease. Prolonged exposure causes rodents to become infertile and homosexual and to eat their young, and, at very loud levels, noise kills them.[16]

Dr. Lester W. Sontag reported to the 1969 AAAS conference on data obtained from experiments which indicate fetal sensitivity to sudden noise. During the final three months, the fetus stirs in the womb in response to sudden noise, for example, a hand clap. A sonic boom, however, can cause it to convulse. Dr. Robert E. Bowman and Dr. Kenneth R. Henry reported at the same conference that the sound of a loud electric bell kills mice.[17] 165 *db* will kill cats and rats.[18] Even if noise

15. Reported in the New York *Post*, February 5, 1971.
16. Reported in the New York *Post*, September 29, 1969.
17. Reported in the New York *Post*, December 29, 1969.
18. *Newsweek*, January 26, 1970.

doesn't kill you outright, enlarged heart and adrenal glands will bring the same end at a slower pace.

Theodore Berland suggests that the infrasound of technological society will pose a greater hazard to human cells in ten years than will atomic fallout.[19]

Sonic energy is the rapid pushing and pulling of air; how frequently this cycle takes place each second determines pitch; how strongly it takes place determines volume, measured in decibels. Our ears can sense cycle frequencies from 16 to 20,000 cycles per second; higher than that, the thin, high whistle seems to become silent but actually the energy is still present as ultrasonic or inaudibly rapid cycles. Dolphins, for example, talk at far above 20,000 cycles. When the pitch falls below 16 cycles, a deep rumble turns to an inaudible vibration. This is infrasonic energy, which still affects us. At 7 cycles, infrasound has been shown to jam human brainwaves and befuddle even simple thinking processes. Stronger or "louder" infrasound causes body tissue such as eyes and internal organs to vibrate with it; turning it up even more leads to headache, nausea, internal hemorrhaging, and death.

Large industrial machines and ventilating equipment often set up infrasonic vibrations; infrasound pollution is common to urban life. In nature, earthquakes and volcanic eruption can also set up infrasonics (a possible reason the citizens of Pompeii were overwhelmed is that they might have been too fuddled to escape). Professor Vladimar Gavreau, head of the French government's Electro-Acoustic Laboratory at the National Scientific Research Center in Marseilles, has patented an infrasonic acoustical laser, a silent death ray, which is surprisingly

19. Theodore Berland, *The Fight for Quiet* (Englewood Cliffs: Prentice-Hall, 1970).

simple and cheap to make. The French Defense Department is studying the military applications.

We are only beginning to learn the dimensions of noise pollution. Studied European factory workers exposed to noise tend toward abnormal heart rhythms and irregular brainwave patterns. Noise is now believed to affect hormonal balance through the central nervous system, thereby throwing metabolism off kilter and opening the way for disease. It seems obvious that excessive noise acts as a dieback mechanism. Because we have never experienced such noise levels before, we cannot know what it does until we can study the damage in retrospect—after it is too late.

The fondness of the young for rock music (when live, around 120 *db*) is making them increasingly deaf. A Mabaan tribesman of the Sudan has better hearing at seventy-five than does the average American twenty-five-year-old. Rock isn't "noise" (unpleasant sound) to its audience, but it still erodes hearing. Perhaps there is an unconscious survival motive in this self-inflicted deafness.

Because the engine noise of the SST is so high (up to 124 *db*), it is important to keep it out of our lives. Even *if* flown subsonic across land, its booms and their infrasonic "echo" over water could disturb migratory patterns of fish, as well as cause other damage in the frail arctic environment. Even with the defeat of government funding, we should keep alert to prevent the addition of foreign commercial SST noise. For more information, contact:

Citizens League Against the Sonic Boom
19 Appleton Street
Cambridge, Massachusetts 02138

Let the airlines know you will never use an SST if it's ever introduced. The conventional jet noise around our airports is alone destroying many lives; over forty Los Angeles schools must suspend teaching or studying every few minutes as a jet roars overhead to or from nearby L.A. International Airport. On Long Island, neighbors of La Guardia and especially Kennedy International have grown increasingly desperate; one harried resident cried that if only there was blood coming from his ears his situation might be taken seriously. Around New York, at least two groups are battling the noise burden:

Town and Village Aircraft Noise Abatement
    Committee
Lawrence, Long Island

Citizens for a Quieter City
136 East 57th Street
New York City

If you live in a city, there are almost certainly several antinoise leagues; contact them through any environmental action group to see how you can help, or write your mayor's office for their names.

But jets are by no means the major noise pollutant— common everyday traffic provides an estimated 85 percent, heightened by sirens, horns, trucks, and compresser-engine roar. Why don't our subways have rubber wheels as in Montreal—or at least plastic foam sprayed in the tunnels to absorb the roar and shriek? Why aren't there simple noise ordinances to force construction and street repair equipment to be of the new quieter, but slightly more expensive types? Why don't our cars have soft city and louder highway horns, as in France?

Why do building codes permit low ceilings and thin walls in an environment where people still controlled by stress come home to yell at each other or dissolve their fear and tension in the roar of the stereo or television?

If your house has a yard, remember that trees soak up noise, as do lawns. Their natural rustling is soothing in itself and also helps absorb certain other noises through the "white sound" effect. Just as white light is composed of all colors of light, white sound is composed of all audible sound frequencies; thus, any sound which is itself the same or less volume will seem to vanish as it is absorbed. Rushing mountain streams are another natural source of nearly white sound. Electronic white sound generators are used to induce and ensure sleep; no one was ever kept awake by a rushing stream or a rustling tree. Trees would be invaluable acoustic sponges for noisy downtown areas.

Other noise-reducing tips: Get carpeting, drapes, acoustic tile, overstuffed furniture, and other sound-spongy things. Put a thick foam rubber pad under your mixer or blender. Submarines—diesel engines, generators, fans, pumps, compressers—are all metal and could be the noisiest things under water; but they are designed to be almost utterly quiet. So are reconnaissance planes. So could your blender or any other noisy piece of equipment.

Stress has been recently shown to activate latent infectious disease in animals and people. Cattle and sheep get shipping fever from the stress of being transported. Pigs that showed no sign of being infected were taken for truck rides in a recent experiment; whether or not the pigs "knew" the ride was one-way to the slaughterhouse, the stress of transport brought on active salmonella infection in 30 percent. Pigs awaiting slaughter have high rates of salmonella infection; pigs still on the farm do not. Salmonella in humans has increased 10 times as the noise level quadrupled since 1950. Stress has been shown to "awaken" cholera in people who've just tested as negative to the germ. A healthy individual leaving a cholera-infested area can be a carrier who, upon undergoing stress, can spread the infection in other areas. The role played by urban stress in the epidemic spread of urban influenza in recent years is undetermined, but it wouldn't be surprising if it were major.

Aside from making less noise ourselves, especially at night and pressing for ordinances to minimize night noise—at least from 11 P.M. to 7 A.M.—one of our best defenses against stress is simply to recognize that it's there and try not to be controlled by it. Look at the faces around you next time you're in a crowded, loud, stressful situation. Once you recognize how others are reacting—shouting, pushing, rushing, leaning on car horns, muttering to themselves—you're relieved of some blind alarm responses. Though it isn't a complete defense, remaining calm in and conscious of the environment can help preserve you from it, and lowering stress may reduce the degree to which chemical pollutants debilitate you.

Poisoning the Last Well

Japan may be the most industrialized nation on earth; with half our population its islands aggregate a land mass only about the size of Montana. Two-thirds of its people live in a 400-mile-long coastal megalopolis, the densest concentration of people in the world, extending from Tokyo to Hiroshima. The air is so bad, the cities so crowded, the suburbs so ugly that John B. Oakes suggests that the New York–Washington corridor almost looks like a planned development in comparison; his article was carried under the following subhead: Ecological Hiroshima May Engulf a People in Pursuit of G.N.P.[20]

Japan's gross national product is the third largest in the world and the fastest-rising. It will pass the Soviet Union's and is projected to equal and possibly even surpass that of the United States before the century is out. The Japanese goal is empire without military expense through the adopted Western drives of business and production. Compared to the Japanese, we are rather lazy. Infusing Western drive and technology into a people so capable of dedication and zeal has resulted in their superpollution. Japan's once fabulous Inland Sea, now ringed with chemical factories, is as dead as Lake Erie.

Cadmium, a heavy metal like lead and mercury, is a serious environmental hazard. The Journal of the American Medical Association carried a report by Dr. Robert E. Carroll in 1966 which showed the cadmium concentration in the air over twenty-eight American cities to vary in proportion to the death rates from high blood pressure and arteriosclerotic heart disease.[21] It also damages kidneys.

Cadmium comes from certain industrial processes, such as zinc plating, but we also get it in bleached flour, refined rice, and acidic soft water. It also is discharged into

20. "Can Japan Survive Its Own Success?" John B. Oakes, *New York Times*, October 11, 1970.

21. Reported in the *New York Times*, November 22, 1970.

the environment from gasoline, tires, and heating and lubricating oil. Cadmium can concentrate directly in our body or be stored for us by plants and animals. Even very minuscule amounts can lead to high blood pressure.

Cadmium is believed to be a major factor in high blood pressure problems confronting 23 million Americans, according to Dr. Henry A. Schroeder, professor of physiology at Dartmouth Medical School and director of its Trace Element Laboratory. In a report to a Senate subcommittee headed by Senator Philip A. Hart, cardiovascular death rates were directly related to the amount of cadmium in drinking water. Dr. Schroeder told the Senate: "I must emphasize that environmental pollution by toxic metals is a much more serious and more insidious problem than is pollution by organic substances such as pesticides, weed killers, sulfur dioxide, and other gross contaminants of air and water." [22]

Fortunately, our environment is not yet cadmium-poisoned to the point that it causes death directly. To see what larger concentrations do, look at Japan, the first nation to diagnose the "Itai, Itai" ("ouch, ouch") disease as cadmium poisoning. The disease progressively weakens the bones through loss of calcium until even standing causes painful bone fractures. About a hundred persons have so far died from the disease.

In America, cadmium poisoning is not yet a direct lethal hazard except to workers exposed to high levels in plating and other metal-working processes; when cadmium fumes are inhaled, severe lung inflammation, coughing, and difficult breathing result. One in five victims dies; the fumes are so toxic that we reportedly have considered it for chemical warfare.[23]

22. Reported in the *New York Times*, August 27, 1970.
23 Reported in the *New York Times*, September 20, 1970.

For another picture of water pollution, we look again to Japan. *Mainichi Shimbun*, a Tokyo newspaper, recently featured a photograph whose negative was developed only in water collected from rivers and canals near Mount Fuji. Photographic developers are complicated alkaline solutions, but these streams are so fouled that their water contains the chemicals which approximate the action of photographic developer.

Israel, like Japan, is a vigorously developing nation which is destroying its water supply, in this case, the famous and, to many people, sacred, Sea of Galilee. Aerial "dog fights" have littered the sea's bottom with artillery shells; the shores are a ring of tourist litter and debris. Airplanes crop-dusting nearby fields continually sift pesticides into the water, and fertilized irrigation water, high BOD drainage from fishponds, industrial waste and municipal sewage flow into the water either directly or via the Jordan River. The Galilee is eutrophying from nitrogen and phosphorus from the thousands of tons of waste which may make its 77 square miles undrinkable within five years. Almost all Israelis depend at least in part on the Sea of Galilee for drinking water: an entire nation is poisoning its chief well.

The wells are already poisoned for over half the human race, for the most part by human wastes which have resulted in our current global cholera pandemic. In Thailand, where only a tenth of the population has piped water, water-borne disease causes 60 percent of illnesses and 40 percent of deaths. William Wood of the World Health Organization noted recently that "if just a tenth of one percent of this situation existed in North America or Europe, we would be scared stiff, but it's nothing in underdeveloped countries." [24]

24. Reported in the *New York Times*, September 20, 1970.

As we know, we pollute more of the fresh water flowing into Earth's ultimate well than half of the rest of the human race. If you or your group would like to move beyond just reducing personal pollution, why not consider direct action with the 1899 Refuse Act? To present your local federal attorney with evidence which will stand in court, it should include the following:

1. location and name of the offender
2. a description of the source and method of discharge
3. a definition in general terms of the discharged waste
4. the name of the waterway being dumped into
5. the date or dates upon which the discharge was witnessed
6. names and addresses of witnesses
7. if possible, photographs and a sample of the waste, labeled to tie into the above 6 points, as well as the name of the person who took the picture or collected the sample (which witness), how the evidence was gotten, and who kept the evidence until it was presented in court
8. proof that the waterway is navigable (smaller streams may require a lawyer's help in being defined navigable, but most of our burdened rivers are simple to prove)
9. a statement that the discharge has not been authorized by the Army Corps of Engineers*

For more detailed information, write Representative Henry Reuss in Washington. His committee will mail

* Gladwin Hill, in the *New York Times*, December 28, 1970, noted that the Corps of Engineers have not, since 1899, issued even one permit. The Corps is, however, planning to begin issuing permits.

a copy of the act as well as an outline for proceeding. The 50 percent share you receive of any collected fines makes an appropriate bounty.

For other information on catching industrial polluters, write:

> Hudson River Fisherman's Association
> P.O. Box 725
> Ossining, New York 10562

The HRFA supplies "Bag-a-Polluter" cards for reporting violations. Get some; learn to use them.

Environmental law is the most rapidly growing area of the legal profession, attracting growing numbers of law students and young lawyers who are disgusted with their profession being mainly a service affiliate of industry. The American Bar Association recently issued a committee report opposed to consumer class-action suits against defrauding corporations—nine of the committee's members also served industry or trade organizations. A similar area of conflicting interest was revealed in a nationwide investigation by the *New York Times* reported by Gladwin Hill on December 7, 1970. Most of the state antipollution boards—thirty-five of them— are weighted with representatives of the polluting industries.

Not long ago, the nation was shocked by the FDA finding of mercury in over 23 percent of its tuna supply. Dr. Bruce McDuffie, who made the initial discovery, found even greater amounts in swordfish. Both species are pelagic—that is, their mercury was concentrated in food chains at deep levels far from shore.

Although the FDA announced that one would have to eat two cans of contaminated tuna every day for a year before being poisoned, and Commissioner Charles C.

Edwards announced of the tainted tuna, "This is not a health hazard"; it is very much an extinction hazard. Although we know how much mercurized fish we can tolerate we do not know how much mercury from other sources is contributing to the final dose. We have only just discovered the mercury in game birds, seals, lobsters, fish, and the air; what further surprises are in store? The contamination level will increase as more and more mercury is added to pelagic—indeed, global—food chains, where it will remain for a century. Developing fetuses have a 30 percent greater affinity for absorbing mercury than their mothers. Mercury inhibits photosynthesis in oceanic plankton, as does DDT: the base of the world's food chain and 70 percent of its oxygen production are involved.

Clearly, the sources of the mercury must be shut off as rapidly as possible. Even if it stopped today, we would not know for many years the final extent of what has already been done. A new organization which should certainly soon become a national force has been formed; contact:

The Stop Ocean Dumping Association
Wildwood, New Jersey

When the Army obtained permission from the Senate to dump 12,540 rockets containing GB nerve gas into the Atlantic in August, 1970, what the approving Senate didn't know was that the shipment also included five quarts of VX. VX is about 40 times as potent as GB, and the ten pounds which were involved are sufficient to sterilize 50 to 200 square miles of all lifeforms. The obsolete Bolt rockets, containing war gases, also contain a solid fuel which tends to become unstable with age and can explode underwater, however, and when they do, the cache of VX will also be released to mingle with the tons of nerve gas dumped into the sea by Germany and almost all the nations which made the Allied Powers of World War II. Mustard gas dumped into the North Atlantic after World War I has been leaking out and is responsible for the death of tens of thousands of sea birds to date. Total damage to the ocean system from our fifty years of dumping military gases will not be known until the destruction is sufficiently advanced to then be further predicted.

Will our poisons weaken species of food fish so they cannot survive our overfishing? Will the mercury and DDT work with the herbicides to destroy plankton, the life base of the world? What are the million tons of oil doing to the food chain? What of the Pacific, whose lead content increased 1000 percent since 1940?

We look upon our poisonings as if they were isolated, not cumulative or synergistic. The actions are so often in secret. The AEC works in secret, assuring us that they understand what they're doing; and one morning (December 19, 1970) we read that an underground bomb test went awry and blew a cloud of radioactive dust 8,000 feet into the air.

How are we to believe the AEC after their history of gaffes, when they also assure us of the safety of nuclear energy?

The Federal Environmental Protection Administration arrives at its conclusions in secret, releasing their data only after releasing their decision.

The Army dumped VX in secret, they spilled a cupful of anthrax germs in Utah in secret, killing wildlife. They leaked nerve gas in Skull Valley, Idaho, a few years ago, which killed 11,000 sheep and cattle, yet maintained their secrecy even after it was plain that they were responsible (they subsequently admitted it).

Industry refuses to yield pollution data on the grounds that trade secrets would be jeopardized. California agricultural corporations will not yield data on what type or how much pesticide is being used on their fields, or even how recently it was used, although people have died in these fields from these poisons.

None of the above are secret to the sea. We may forget the AEC blowout, but the environment is a little less stable for it, just as it is less stable because of the Santa Barbara oil blowout. A global marine catastrophe will be no secret, and we've noted its beginning.

Wildlife and the Smell of Smoke: The Final Chapter

"Man's genetically controlled attributes are essentially in phase with the changes in other organisms around him, but his learned patterns are so completely out of phase with the slow process of evolution that he threatens himself and all creatures."
—Dr. Charles M. Allen, professor of biology and president of the North Carolina Academy of Science[25]

The Fouke Fur Company has a monopoly contract with the Interior Department for the entire annual slaughter of Alaskan fur seals on the Pribilof Islands. A recent Fouke ad read: "*Fur Seal—So much rarer than mink.*" This, sadly enough, is true. Fouke also runs ads, reportedly subsidized by the Interior Department, which

25. Reported in the *Winston-Salem Journal*, May 2, 1970.

try to explain why it is good for the seals to be killed: although nature has been balancing those seal herds since they began, man (and especially the Interior Department) is actually better at it than nature. This, sadly enough, is not true. Mother Nature, for one thing, doesn't own a sealskin coat. Natural attrition strengthens a herd by removing the weakest. Man, conversely, wants only the finest coats and takes the finest specimens. The process is very profitable for Fouke, especially as it's subsidized with tax money.

There was a great public clamor when TV showed the clubbing and skinning of baby seals; sometimes they were skinned alive. These were Canadian seals, not Alaskan, so it took time, but eventually the practice was changed in some areas to shooting rather than clubbing. According to Dr. Roger R. Payne, the biologist who made the first stereo recording of whales singing, so many of the wounded older seals escape, only to die slowly in the frigid water, that about three times as many seals—many of them pregnant—are being killed as formerly were being clubbed.[26] "Humanely killed" or not, the Canadian Atlantic and Gulf of St. Lawrence seal herds have been reduced by one-third in the past twenty years, and continue to diminish. Sealers, who pay $1 for a license to kill 1,000 seals, often kill three times the maximum number recommended. Often we're told that their livelihood depends on the killing, but in recent years the average seasonal earning has wavered between $39 and $102—someone *else* is making the profit. Why not just avoid sealskin, especially white (baby) fur; give the bright creatures a break and help eliminate the profit and the slaughter.

26. Reported in the New York *Post*, November 27, 1970.

Spending $400 for an impala shirt—made from the entire skin, legs, tail, and all—at the oddly named Resurrection Shop at Georges Kaplan in New York may seem a satire on barbarism, but the shirt is there if you want it. Still, only one impala is needed for each shirt, whereas about forty raccoons go into every coat. Forty million open-leg steel-jawed traps are always waiting for victims all over North America. Trapped animals, maddened by agony, often chew off their own legs trying to escape the pain. Now that the alligator is almost extinct, frogs are looked to be one of the "in" skins of the 1970s.[27] In view of the dwindling supply of domestic frogs for biology classes and gourmets' palates, perhaps the "in" skin of the 80s will be exoskeleton of roach.

A few winters ago at a ranch in Montana, a rancher's teen-age sons returned from rabbit hunting. Hunting had been good, they said, they'd gotten fifteen "VC"; the furry little "Viet Cong" hadn't been picked up, simply left to remain where they fell. We read reports of teenage helicopter pilots in Vietnam who fire rockets into bushes, then gun down the civilians as they run for better cover. We are shocked to read of our soldiers bedecking their helmets and radio aerials with human ears and genitalia, and wonder where such barbarism comes from, but insensitivity to human life is really only the logical extension of killing any life for "pleasure."

Rabbits eat some of the baled hay around Mud Lake, Idaho; consequently, the local ranchers organize "rabbit bops." Snow fences funnel the driven rabbits, 6,000 on one televised occasion, into large chickenwire pens where, as shown by Walter Cronkite, they are beaten to death by laughing children.[28] Similar "bunny bops" have been conducted by the American Legion Post in Harmony,

27. Paul Swatek, *User's Guide*, p. 244.
28. CBS News, February 16, 1970.

North Carolina; tickets are sold and the profits go to charity.

NBC's TV special, "Slaughtering the Seals," presented on January 23, 1971, showed the action on the Pribilof Islands. The Alaskan seals are driven inland until they drop from exhaustion, then they are clubbed and skinned; all this was shown as the narrator explained how it was really in the best interests of the seals that they were being killed (Fouke didn't sponsor the show, surprisingly enough). Perhaps worse than seeing the flayed corpses and hearing the clubs strike the skulls was seeing the expressions of excitement and glee on the faces of the tourists, men and women, who charter a bus for the specific "treat" of seeing the slaughter.

Yet, is this any worse than stampeding the vanishing Western mustang by airplane, then killing and selling them at 6 cents a pound for pet food? At the current rate of killing, the mustang is expected to be a rarity for only eight more years, after which it will be a nonentity. Kangaroos are similarly killed for Japanese and American pet food. Polar bears, caribou, eagles—anything more mobile or clever than man is hunted by plane, and we are only now beginning to question the "sport."

Each year deer hunters and sport equipment retailers decry the plight of "starving" deer in local wildlife preserves, and too often, the hunters are permitted an open season in order to "protect" the animals. Modern hunters are notoriously bad shots, and many more deer are wounded than killed; of those wounded, an estimated two out of three escape to die in slow agony. In all, about a billion wild animals are fatally wounded each year.[29] Many ranchers post their land not to protect the

---

29. Mel Morse, *Ordeal of the Animals* (Englewood Cliffs: Prentice-Hall, 1968), pp. 98–102.

deer, but to keep hunters from using their livestock for practice. Idaho spends $4,000 a month replacing road signs used as warm-up targets by hunters waiting their chance at a "starving" doe. Where the lack of natural predators will allow deer populations to exceed the carrying capacity of their range the herds should be thinned by trained wildlife management officials who tranquilize the animals for shipment to areas where deer are scarce. If the animals must be shot, it should be by game officials who would take only the weak as would natural predation. Hunters are unable and unwilling to do this. We similarly kill 30 to 50 percent of our duck and goose population yearly. With neither deer nor fowl does the birth rate equal the death rate. Even rabbits, which increase 900 percent annually, are on the decrease in twenty-five states, and in these states their natural predators are nearly extinct.[30] This means, of course, that it is the American sportsman again, or worse, a child for whom the difference between slaughter and laughter is only the "s".

Our greatest state for wolves is in Alaska, where there are only about 5,000. They are hunted from the air. In the "lower" 48 states, the last few are killed by poisoned baits, as are eagles, condors, coyotes, bear, cougar, lynx, bobcat, and other scavenger and predator species. The bounty program is a mistake, particularly now. Natural predation is a vital balance in nature; far from being bountied, these creatures deserve protection. Before Richard Ottinger left the House of Representatives, he introduced legislation to protect many North American predators. His legislation reportedly is in trouble; write

30. George L. Herter and Berthe E. Herter, *How to Get Out of the Rat Race and Live on $10 a Month* (Waseca: Herters, 1965), p. 605.

your Representative and urge his support for the Ottinger bill, H.R. 13429.

We have a negative feeling toward predators, perhaps dating to the past when we were prey ourselves. The late Joseph Wood Krutch wrote: "When a man wantonly destroys one of the works of man we call him Vandal. When he wantonly destroys one of the works of God we call him Sportsman."

Where, one wonders, is the sport in luring coyotes to a terrified sheep staked on a frozen lake, then running down the hungry animal with a pack of snowmobiles? Snowmobile hunting is drawing thousands of new devotees yearly. It is long past time for us to outlaw killing wildlife for fun.

The American Automobile Association issued a report in 1968 which concluded that "we kill more game with our cars than our hunters do with guns." According to the AAA, 365 million wild animals are killed on the highway each year: a million a day. Although it isn't always easy to avoid an animal suddenly on the highway, I have seen drivers deliberately swerve to hit smaller ones.*

Sometimes we do to animals what we are impotent to do to humans; animals in the New York Central Park Zoo must spend their nights indoors because when left in their outdoor cages, people stab them with knives or pointed wires, or feed them apples containing needles or shards of broken glass.

We rub out wildlife through sheer meanness of spirit. Hundreds of millions of prairie dogs have been poisoned so our cattle can have the grass the highly social rodents

---

* Friends of Animals provides a large fluorescent bumper sticker which reads: WARNING! I BRAKE FOR ANIMALS.

would otherwise consume. Australian ranchers, furious because kangaroos remain sleek on land where sheep cannot thrive, simply shoot them. At 1.5 million killed annually, it's certain that the kangaroo will not last as long as our meanness. Deer are not allowed in Wales; they eat grass without producing beef. Green Sea Turtles have been taken off our endangered species list not because they are in no danger, but because little is known of their migratory patterns and, as they all concentrate on a few beaches to lay eggs, it appears that they must be numerous. The marvelous big sea turtle, which science is studying, trying to learn how they can migrate 6,000 miles from a tiny scrap of sand beach, then return to it years later, is facing extinction because of gourmets who like soup and ladies who rub turtle oil on their skin.

Corporate farming operations in Ash Meadows, California, divert water otherwise bound in a trickle to Death Valley. The water is only a few inches deep and generally about 93 degrees, but it's the only home of the Devil's Hole Pupfish, of which there is one school of two hundred, unique upon the earth. The corporate farming will dry up as soon as the water does—about five years—but in the meantime an entire species will have been driven to extinction.

Because of passive or "listening" sonar, we have only recently learned that whales and dolphins have elaborate languages and that they communicate in a way as sophisticated as human language, and possibly more. Dolphins are now known to be sapient creatures. Russians, who call them "comrade dolphin" in recognition of their intelligence, have outlawed killing them. People who work with them always note how trusting of men they are; we are learning to actually break their language code and communicate with them; some scientists feel they are perhaps *more* intelligent than humans. Our Navy conducts extensive dolphin research, and recently shipped three dolphins to Vietnam for classified duty[31]—perhaps to detect enemy frogmen, perhaps to be "kamikaze" torpedoes.

Humpback whales communicate by singing complex songs, some of short duration, others very long. The song cycles are often repeated, and even the longest are repeated "word for word" every time. Each song is different from all the others, sometimes sounding like electronic music, sometimes like sitar music. It is believed that whales can hear one another sing although they may be miles, perhaps hundreds of miles, apart. Their songs also apparently are a guide in their global migrations. Whales are being urgently studied while they last—no one knows how some survive dives to 7,000 feet where pressure is so great that air in a human lung would be compressed into fluid. Scientists are afraid that the noise level of the oceans is rising to the point where it will jam the whalesong—like static. To a whale, a ship's propeller a few miles away might be a confusing cacophony.*

Former Interior Secretary Walter J. Hickel had the extraordinary foresight to put whales on the protected list *before*, not after, the last gasp—he saw the list's

---

31. WCBS News, New York, December 22, 1970.
* A beautiful stereo record of whalesong along with a superb booklet telling of whales and their plight is available from *Whales*, CRM Books, Communications Research Machines Inc., P.O. Box 60332, Los Angeles, California 90060. Perhaps the best book on the whale and dolphin world is Victor B. Scheffer's *The Year of the Whale* (New York: Charles Scribner's Sons, 1969), available in paperback.

function as being preventive, not commemorative. The Nixon administration, after removing Secretary Hickel, reversed his ban on whales.[32] Whales have since been reinstated on the list. The American whale industry (mostly comprised of the Archer Daniels Midland Company of Decatur, Illinois, and Werner G. Smith, Inc., of Cleveland) had lobbied intensely for such a reversal, contending that the oil of sperm whales is "essential to national defense." Whale oil is used in lipstick, shoe polish, transmissions, dog and cat food, soap, fertilizer, margarine, hand cream, and other similarly "essential" products. How do we defend ourselves with whale oil? Write Interior Secretary Morton and ask him to reinstate the ban.

The International Whaling Commission is dominated by the world whaling industry, and quotas have always been scandalously high; for example, although scientists say that no more than 4,000 sperm whales can be "harvested" annually without eliminating the species, the Commission's 1970 quota was for over 13,500. Even this overkill quota doesn't mean that "only" 9,500 too many were taken, because several of the major whaling nations, the Soviet Union notably, refuse to allow international observers to inspect their operations.[33]

Even medical research contributes to extinction; Dr. Lyndon E. Lee, assistant chief medical director for research and education in medicine for the Veterans Administration urges researchers to not use so many monkeys, chimpanzees, baboons, and apes for research projects because the heavy drain is bringing these species close to extinction.

Our reckless pollution joins with our hypocrisy, bar-

32. Reported in the New York Times, November 28, 1970.
33. Time, July 13, 1970.

barism, bloodlust, and greed to decimate wildlife. Many examples of general pollution harming wildlife have been given; several million sea birds and billions of other living things die in oil pollution each year, for instance, but perhaps as significant: dead seals have been washing up on the Cornish coast with red burn marks the size of saucers. The burns are actually infections caused by Pasteurella, a bacteria which spawns in polluted waters and which biologists fear will kill all seal pups in the area.

Thousands of ducks and other waterfowl die of lead poisoning each year; they mistake spent shotgun pellets for seed and need eat only three to five of the tiny pellets to become sterile and die. Draining marshes to provide irrigation draws down the water level, exposing fetid mud bottoms with their botulism-producing organisms to the birds. Epidemic deaths from botulism sweep waterfowl populations every year. The decimation will increase if the Nixon administration proceeds with its plan to sell off 2.8 million acres of National Wildlife Refuge for commercial development. As it is, the Refuge system supported 541,000 hunting visits in 1966 and is continually under pressure to open up more fully. In the middle of one such preserve in Kansas, a sportsman's club has built a permanent duck blind with built-in heating—the comforts of home. The Army uses several Wildlife Refuges for artillery ranges; Amchitka Island, site of the controversial underground hydrogen bomb tests, is one of the few "protected" homes for the imperiled sea otter.

As the marshlands shrink and disappear, ducks and other waterfowl must concentrate in the few areas which remain; sportsmen cite these concentrated flocks as evidence that duck populations are growing and must be "controlled." Waterfowl populations are in general decreasing by 8 percent a year.

Organizations working for the preservation of wildlife should receive as much support as we have time and money. Most of the conservation groups listed earlier are active in this struggle. An affiliate of Friends of Animals, listed earlier, is:

Committee for Humane Legislation
11 West 60th Street
New York City 10023

This group works for domestic as well as wild animal welfare.

Friends of Animals suggests that *whenever* you see a TV documentary on cruelty to animals or the plight of wildlife, that you write the sponsor and the network. Thank them and ask that they repeat the program. One such documentary is "Say Goodbye," sponsored by:

Quaker Oats Company
345 Merchandise Mart Plaza
Chicago, Illinois 60654

This moving wildlife extinction film was shown early in 1971. Be wary, however, of any film which suggests in any way that it is good for the animal to be killed—as did the NBC special on the Alaskan fur seal. FOA provides films free for group showings. "Not Born Free" is about the Pribilof Island (or Alaskan fur) seal, and "S591" is about animal slaughter. Give a date at least two weeks ahead and, if you can, an alternate date. Contact the nearest outlet of:

Association Films Inc.
(East)   600 Grand Avenue
Ridgefield, N.J. 07657

(Mid-West) 512 Burlington Avenue
            La Grange, Illinois 60525

(West) 25358 Cypress Avenue
        Hayward, California 94544

(South) 8615 Directors' Row
         Dallas, Texas 75247

Friends of Animals is, with the Committee for Humane Legislation, actively seeking support for five important bills (being drafted at this writing) which will be introduced in Congress in 1971. The bills will cover:

Protection for Mammals of the Oceans
Protection of Wildlife on Federal Public Lands
Protection of Fur-Bearing Animals
Reducing the Suffering of Livestock in Slaughter
Elimination of Cruelty to Animals in Schools

Cruelty is the only element which will be put out of business by any of these bills if they are passed, none of them is "unrealistic" or "crankish." FOA doesn't solicit funds, although they exist on contributions and will continue to send you reports and action letters urging immediate individual, local, or national action.[34] And don't forget the motto, available on an FOA lapel button: BOYCOTT FUR BEARING PEOPLE.

Outfits to inform that you will boycott and will urge your friends to boycott and support legislation to eliminate their wild fur trade include:

National Assn. of Importers and Exporters of Hides
  & Skins
225 Broadway
New York City

34. See p. 154.

American Fur Merchants Association, Inc.
224 West 30th Street
New York City

The Fouke Company
Route 1, Box 168
Greenville, South Carolina 29611

Many college students now greet people wearing wild furs with admonitions of shame, or by muttering "how gross" and other sentiments as they pass on the street. If this type of thing appears rude to you, consider the lack of politeness of a steel-toothed leg trap, or how crude it is to wear the skin of a being who, like you, enjoyed being alive.

Saving wildlife is *not* a sentimental goal; our own survival depends on it if for no other reason than that, once the wild animals are gone, we will have no index as to our pollution and may pollute ourselves very rapidly to death. Recall that the alerts on DDT and mercury were sounded by the early discovery of these substances in wildlife. We can consume all the oil and iron and we will be poor, but if we consume all the wild creatures, we will be alone on this planet, subject to the same drives which destroyed the wild creatures.

We can have no food chains without those chains having links, and we have for some time been destroying them rapidly. David Brower of Friends of the Earth observed in a recent advertisement against the trans-Alaska pipeline and the inevitable, colossal wildlife devastation it will produce, "There is also some human self-interest involved here. If we destroy enough we may do ourselves in. Everything works together. W. C. Fields once put it this way: 'If there ain't no chickens, Harry, there ain't no eggs.' " [35] If we kill the biotic film, then it can't be there—and neither will we be, shortly thereafter.

Yet, if we have played a role on earth, it has been as the Great Eliminator. Man's presence on earth has increased the extinction potential for all species by 400 percent. The actual arithmetic may be greater than that, for of all the species earth has ever fostered, only man has ever driven another species to exinction. During the past century, 90 percent of Africa's wildlife has been destroyed. Since 1700, we have extirpated 290 species of vertebrates, half of them since 1900; the pace is quickening every year. At least 860 races of mammals, birds, fish, and reptiles face extinction almost immediately, and the list grows in proportion with increases in human population and consumption.

Controlling human increase is finally the only way we will salvage not only wildlife, but our own future. One new American consumer every 8 seconds is probably a greater threat to wildlife than a thousand Sunday hunters. And we must break out of the psychological lockstep of purchase and consumption. This is not freedom; the compulsive consumer is an economic slave. Dr. Richard A. Falk, professor of International Law at Princeton University noted recently, "If the United States were to double its Gross National Product, I would think it would be a much less livable society than it is today." [36] To even maintain the present level of ecodestruction will require spending $40 billion yearly, or 4 percent of our GNP; to *begin* reversing the plague we have brought

35. Advertisement in the *New York Times*, February 17, 1971.

36. Reported by Sylvia Porter in the New York *Post*, February 10, 1971.

upon our planet will cost at least $60 to $80 billion each year.[37] Costly, yes. We'd have to abandon our adventures overseas—but as the technological leader of our species, and the epicenter of the plague it has become, do we have any choice but to commit all our resources for survival? Prince Phillip, the Duke of Edinburgh and James Fisher wrote of our peril, in *Wildlife Crisis*:

"Whenever any animal or plant population reaches plague proportions, it destroyed its own living space and supply of food and died. If it did not die out entirely, at least it was drastically reduced. This could happen to mankind."

This is dieback, noted earlier, and the species of man has become a plague. Zero Population Growth and Planned Parenthood/World Population are listed earlier; contact them, join their efforts. Other groups:

> Association for Voluntary Sterilization
> 14 West 40th Street
> New York City 10018

> Population Council
> 245 Park Avenue
> New York City 10017

> Campaign to Check the Population Explosion
> Hugh Moore Fund
> 60 East 42nd Street
> New York City 10017

The Hugh Moore Fund sends out a free clipping abstract, a periodic bulletin of articles from papers around the country which deal with population issues; they also recommend new books. As Ramsey Clark pointed out,

37. Ibid.

there are today more Americans living in desperate poverty than the entire population of our country at the end of the Civil War.[38] Yet, on balance, Americans then had more reason to believe poverty could be wiped out than do we today: they had just ended the slave system, had a frontier, and resource depletion was unknown, as was overpopulation. But we must be realistic about the limits of our world: if you believe you can love and raise more than two children, adopt the others. If you cannot locate an adoption center near you, write:

Adoption Resources Exchange of North America
44 East 23rd Street
New York City 10010

It is now believed that man began his career as Great Eliminator about 11,000 years ago when he invented the Clovis point—the sharpened stone spear tip which enabled us to kill large animals such as camels and mastodons. What began with the Clovis point has accelerated with suburban developments, industrial and municipal pollution, highway construction, and agriculture. It is this crude elbowing of more room and more from the ecosystem for our out-of-control population that truly spells the end for wilderness and wild animals. Walter Sullivan, science editor for the *New York Times*, asks, "Will this process continue until virtually no wildlife are left? Will ours become a 'one-crop planet'—the single crop being Homo sapiens, exposed to all the epidemic dangers that threaten one-crop regimes?" [39]

We must learn not only of mercy, but of the nature of the animals themselves. Perhaps then we would have

38. Ramsey Clark, *Crime in America* (New York: Simon & Schuster, 1970).

39. Walter Sullivan, the *New York Times*, March 22, 1970.

at least sufficient respect for them to *leave them alone.*
Ancient Romans drove red-hot skewers through live pigs,
thinking the meat would be more flavorful if the creature
endured as much pain as long as possible before it died.
How stupidly barbaric this seems today, yet all someone has to do is tell us that lobsters "don't feel the pain"
of being boiled alive and we are often absolved. It has
lately been shown that lobsters actually have an extremely high sensorium, their percipience and range of
senses exceeds even our own—in fact, lobsters have many
sense organs whose perceptions we cannot even identify.[40]
Lobsters' migratory behavior bears remarkable resem-
blance to ESP—and, of course, it *is* extrasensory perception in terms of our dullness. Far from feeling no
pain as the water comes to a boil, they must feel more
pain than we will ever know. Yet, probably the recent
announcement by the Massachusetts Public Health Department of the mercury hazard in lobster tail will spare
more of them than anything else.

And what of whales and dolphins—we dream of one
day meeting intelligence in space, yet having finally
encountered it on earth, we send it to war or declare its
body oil vital for defense as we drive it into extinction.
"I believe I have found the missing link between animals
and civilized men," Konrad Lorenz once mused, "it is
us."

It is regrettable that this book must end with the ob-
servance that all the reuses for coffee cans will not bring
back the bald eagle, nor will cutting phosphates and
NTA from detergent help the fifty remaining California condors, or even achieving a zero population growth

40. "Migration of the Spiny Lobster," William F. Herrn-
kind, *Natural History,* May, 1970.

restore the Peregrine falcon, the Louisiana pelican, the Caribbean monk seal, or any of the close to 900 species our excess is shoving into that dark and awful hole in reality through which we drove the last passenger pigeon in 1914. All we can hope is that there still may be time to awaken in a world futured with children of all species, and not awaken only to the smell of smoke.

Mankind is a novel experiment of Earth's, its last species to develop; many species have developed their way into a corner and then extinction before us. The truth has always been so obvious that the terror is we have never, as a species, understood that for 366 generations since the Clovis point, each improved hunting weapon was soon used for killing other men. We are the only species which kills everything on earth, including ourselves, by accident or "intelligent" design. We kill predators and are plagued with their prey; we purge intelligent species to extinction for their body oil; we become afraid of our own nerve gasses and, in panic, dump them into the ocean, the womb of all life on Earth. We befuddle all creatures, including ourselves, with our global poisoning and are now as frightened of this as we are of atomic fission, our sharpest Clovis point, which we realize is really best suited for our instantaneous or long term self-destruction. We parade in animal skins in a stupor as to what this implies: that the death of wildlife is only incidental, a symptom, an unintended side effect of the mindless gashing at the fabric of all life as Earth's most bizarre genetic chain hits its 367th generation—"A.D. 2000" —further out of control than ever.

What makes us think we can survive ourselves if more experienced and adaptable wildlife die out entirely because of our insane commitments?